CU00548051

So You Think You're a
NorthEnder?

The Official Preston North End Quiz Book

An Official PNE Publication

So you think you're a NorthEnder?

First Published in 1997
for PNE Publications.
Commercial House, Lowthorpe Road,
Deepdale, Preston PR1 6RU

ISBN 1 874645 36 1

Typeset and designed by Sport in Word Limited, Blackburn, England
Printed by NB Colour Print, Chorley, England

Contents

So You Think You're a NorthEnder?

The aim of this book is to give every North End Fan - young or old, a bit of fun.

There are a variety of quizzes, crosswords and teasers to test your knowledge of your favourite club and some general football ones too.

The quizzes are split into five categories - from very easy (one ★) to extremely hard (five ★★★★★) Unless you're a soccer genius with more reference books than a library we wouldn't expect you to get full marks everytime - but all the answers are here - so even if you can't answer a question you can learn something new about your club!

For those who like a target to aim for or wish to compete against families or friends we suggest that you score questions from different quizzes as follows:

★★★★★ quiz = 5 points
★★★★ quiz = 4 points
★★★ quiz = 3 points
★★ quiz = 2 points
★ quiz = 1 points

now all you have to do is have fun!

The Championship Year 1995-96

It's time to test your recent knowledge of the club. In this particular quiz we take a look back at North End's triumphant march to the Third Division. There are questions concerning games, goals and scorers, so get your thinking caps on.

1. We lost our first home league game to which club?

2. The following Saturday we travelled to one of soccer's far-flung outposts and came away with a 2-0 victory. Who were the opponents?

3. Who were the first Lancashire side we played that season?

4. North End played Bury on Tuesday 29th August at Gigg Lane, what was the final score?

5. In early September we drew 3-3 at Deepdale, with which club?

6. Which North End striker scored the only goal of the game at Hereford on September 9th?

7. In mid September we drew at home to Scunthorpe United. Can you tell us the score?

8. The following week saw North End gain a share of the spoils against which West London side?

9. On October 14th Torquay United were trounced by what score?

10. North End bettered the previous weeks tally when tackling

Mansfield Town seven days later. What score did we win by?

11. Who scored North End's goal in the 1-1 draw at Exeter on November 18th?

12. How many points did we gain from the two league encounters against Chester City?

13. Name the opposition in our last league game before Christmas?

14. On New Years Day we played host to which Welsh club?

15. What was the score of the above match?

16. How many points did Lincoln City gain from their two games against North End?

17. On March 2nd we lost 2-1 at home to which Lancashire Club?

18. Which North End player scored the only goal of the game when we played Cardiff City at Ninian Park in March?

19. North End won their last three games by the same score, what was it?

20. The final league game of the season was played at Deepdale, against which team?

Answers on page 130

Current Squad

This is quite an easy quiz. All you have to do is to name the club from which the following North End players arrived from. (Clue - some are home grown!)

1. Michael Appleton

2. Lee Ashcroft

3. Graeme Atkinson

4. Dean Barrick

5. Julian Darby

6. Simon Davey

7. Sean Gregan

8. Michael Holt

9. Michael Jackson

10. Ryan Kidd

11. Jonathan Macken

12. Tepi

13. Colin Murdock

14. Kurt Nogan

15. Gary Parkinson

16. Mark Rankine

17. David Reeves

18. Paul Sparrow

19. Lee Cartwright

20. Paul McKenna

Answers on page 130

Promotion

It's every manager's dream outside the Premiership to win promotion for their team. By definition, to win promotion you must be in one of the lower leagues, but, getting promoted is still worth it's weight in gold - How many times have North End achieved it? read on and find out...

1. How many times have North End been promoted is it 20, 6 or 9 times?

2. In what season was the club first promoted, was it 1903-4; 1926-27 or 1908-09?

3. What division were we promoted from in that first promotion season?

4. Which local rivals did we play in the final game of that season, was it Accrington Stanley, Darwen or Blackpool?

5. We won that game to secure the Championship, was the score 4-0, 2-1 or 1-0?

6. When North End were promoted to the First Division in 1912-13, which other Lancashire club accompanied them to the top flight?

7. During that promotion season, North End drew how many matches from their first seventeen games, was it 10, 15 or 9?

8. During the same season North End ran up a sequence of how many games without defeat, was it 40, 22 or 15?

9. In what season did North End achieve promotion for the fifth time, Was it 1949/50, 1950/51, or 1951/52?

10. During the same season we managed to go undefeated for how many games, was it 30, 20 or 10?

11. Here are the initials of three members of that successful North End side. Can you identify their full names? T.F., C.W., A.M.

12. In 1970/71, Alan Ball Senior took just one season to secure promotion to Division Two. Name the London ground where we gained the points needed to win promotion?

13. Who scored the winning goal for North End in the same game, was is Spavin, Heppolette, or Robinson?

14. We clinched the Championship three days later with an emphatic 3-0 success against which Yorkshire club?

15. In which year did North End clinch promotion without playing a game?

16. Who was North End's manager when we gained promotion in the 1986-87 season?

17. In that same season, which team did we play in the final league game?

18. Who scored the winner for North End in that same game?

19. North End had two goals disallowed in the same game. Name the player who "scored" them?

20. In 1995-96 promotion was clinched against which North East club?

Answers on page 130

Deepdale

1. In what year did North End move to Deepdale?

2. What name did the club allegedly go under in those days?

3. Name the ground we played at before moving to Deepdale.

4. In the early days, a certain section of society were let into the ground free of charge, who were they?

5. In what year was the North End of the ground developed?

6. And how much did this development cost the club was it £40,000, £2,000 or £19,000?

7. In what year was the Pavilion, opposite the Grandstand built?

8. And in what year was the South Pavilion built?

9. On April 23rd, 1938, North End recorded their highest ever crowd for a clash against which club?

10. Guess the attendance figure for that particular game - 42,684, 51,826, 38,076?

11. In May 1941, Deepdale was taken over by the army in return for how much? £1,056, £1,000, £250?

12. In what year were floodlights first used at Deepdale?

13. In that first floodlit match, North End played against which

Lancashire club?

14. After promotion from the Third Division in 1977-78, the club were required to spend how much on ground improvements? £50,000, £500,000 or £5 million?

15. During the same season, North End had to halt work on ground developments because they ran out of what, tea bags, steel or nails?

16. In what year did North End's historic West Stand get demolished?

17. In what month during 1996 was the Tom Finney Stand opened?

18. Against which club did North End play their final game in front of the Spion Kop before closure?

19. Which royal dignitary visited Deepdale recently?

20. What is the capacity of the Tom Finney Stand? 6,000, 10,000 or 8,000?

Answers on page 131

Highs and Lows

1. During the 1920's PNE managed to score 100 league goals during a particular season. Was it 1927-28; 1928-29 or 1929-30?

2. In season 1957-58, North End found the net 100 times. Two players shared 60 of those goals; can you name either of them?

3. On the two occasions North End have won the FA Cup, they have conceded one solitary goal. Can you name the team we conceded it against?

4. The highest number of goals scored in a League season by a North End player stands at 37. Can you name the player?

5. The lowest number by a "leading" scorer came in 1969-70. Can you name the North End player?

6. The highest attendance for a youth game at Deepdale was 27,764 in 1960 when North End played which London club in the second leg of the FA Youth Cup Final?

7. What was North End's lowest league position during the 1996-97 season?

8. On reaching the FA Cup Final in 1887-88, North End scored a total of 56 goals in seven rounds. How many did they score in the final against West Bromwich Albion?

9. Which famous North End player holds the record for being top scorer in the most number of seasons?

10. Record receipts were taken at the FA Cup third round tie in January 1992 with £68,650 being taken at the gate. Which team were North End playing that day?

11. North End beat which club 10-0 in 1889?

12. Which club beat us 7-0 in 1948?

13. The lowest ever attendance at Deepdale was in the 1980s. Can you name the year?

14. And which team were we playing?

15. The above game was played on a Tuesday afternoon. Why?

16. North End's highest crowd during two seasons in Division Four saw 16,436 pack into Deepdale for a promotion battle in 1986 with which club?

17. The highest number of goals scored in one league match this century came against which Welsh club?

18. How many goals were scored by North End in that 1966 encounter?

19. In the same game North End recorded their lowest gate of the 1965-66 season. What was the gate? Was it 3,167, 7,241 or 10,018?

20. Which North End player scored 30 goals in the 1963-64 season?

Answers on page 131

Crossword (1) answers on page 147

Across

1. North End were one of four League clubs to play on it (7)

6. Former Aston Villa midfielder (4)

7. Full-back who played the last of his 300 League games on Boxing Day 1902 (6)

8. North End's first ....was Frank Lee (10)

10. West German-born defender who made his name with Wolves and Stoke City before playing for Preston (5)

11. .....Atkins who joined the club from Sheffield United (3)

12. .....Allardyce, former North End defender and youth team coach (3)

15. Tony ....much travelled outside-left (7)

16. North End finished runners-up in the ......Division in 1957-58 (5)

17. The Black Prince (6)

Down.

1. Former Sheffield Wednesday winger who appeared in 57 League games for North End in the late 1970s (5)

2. Baxi are North End's (8)

3. Tony Ellis hit a hat-trick against them in 1993-94 in a 4-1 win (12)

4. North End beat them 19-0 in a cup-tie (10)

5. Signed from St Mirren, he went on to win 43 caps for Scotland (7)

9. Former Doncaster Rovers centre-half with foreign-sounding surname (6)

13. Young North End striker (4)

14. Joe .... Glasgow-born defender who appeared in 223 League games (4)

North End lost the 1954 F.A. Cup Final against WBA, 2-3. Fill in the team sheet for the game and the scorers

Answers on page 152

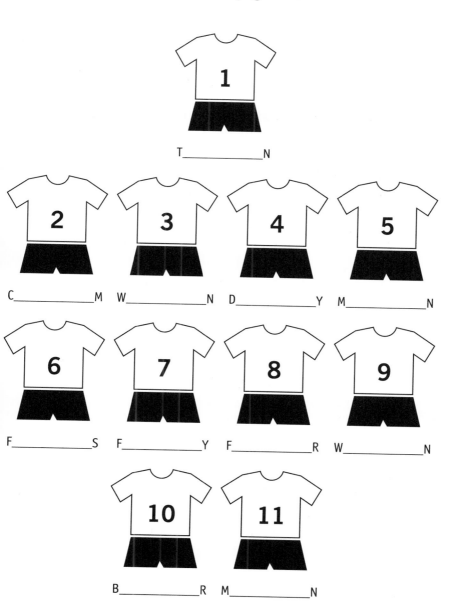

1 T_____N

2 C_____M **3** W_____N **4** D_____Y **5** M_____N

6 F_____S **7** F_____Y **8** F_____R **9** W_____N

10 B_____R **11** M_____N

The League Cup

This quiz will test your knowledge to the full as it puts the spotlight on the "lesser" of the two domestic competitions in this country. Let's see how you get on anyway.

1. Which team knocked North End out of the cup three times in four seasons in the mid-eighties?

2. In 1980/81 North End reached the fourth round to lose to which side in a second replay?

3. In 1971/72 North End lost a replay at home to Spurs, 2-1. Who was North End's scorer?

4. Prior to 1996/97 North End fell at the first round for seven consecutive seasons. Name any 4 of the 7 sides that beat North End?

5. In 38 seasons how many times have North End failed to progress more than one round, is it 16, 18, 20?

6. In the first year of the League Cup, North End went out to the eventual winners - which team?

7. In North End's big run of 1971/72 they started with a win over a club no longer in the league. Which one?

8. Who scored North End's goal in the 1-1 draw against Spurs in 1996/97?

9. In 1987/88 North End lost over two legs to Bury. Who scored for North End in both ties?

10. How many appearances did Tom Finney make in the League Cup?

11. In 1986/87 North End lost to West Ham after drawing 1-1 at Deepdale. What was the score at Upton Park?

12. In 1977/78 North End needed three games to beat which team?

13. In 1980/81 North End went out to WBA after two replays. But who managed the Baggies at the time?

14. In which season did North End last meet Blackpool in the League Cup?

15. Which former North End player was not allowed to play for Rotherham against North End in this year's competition?

16. In 1991/92 North End lost 6-7 on aggregate to Scarborough. Who scored in both legs for North End?

17. North End beat Blackburn Rovers 2-0, over two legs in 1975/76. Tony Morley scored one goal who scored the other?

18. In 1995/96 North End lost 2-3 to Sunderland at Roker Park. Who scored for North End?

19. In 1978/79 North End beat Huddersfield 5-2 on aggregate. Which North End player scored 3 of the goals?

20. Which team then knocked North End out of the competition in 1978/79?

Answers on page 131

The League Cup 1970's

So you think you've done well on that initial League Cup quiz, this is much tougher - see how you do.

1. In the League Cup competition of 1971-72 North End made it to the fourth round where we were eventually beaten by which North London club?

2. In the previous round North End had triumphed 2-1 against which club?

3. The following season 1972-73 saw us go out in the first round to which club?

4. We were again knocked out in the first round the following season to which club?

5. We made it to the third round of the competition in 1974-75 where we were eliminated by which current Third Division club?

6. The 1975-76 League Cup saw the introduction of what, in the first round of the competition?

7. Which Lancashire team did we play in the first round of the 1975-76 competition?

8. We eventually crashed out of the competition that season, to which Yorkshire club?

9. Can you tell us score of the above game, was it 1-0, 2-1, or 4-2?

10. The following season 1976-77 saw North End take on which Lancashire outfit in the first round?

11. It took a replay in the first round of the 1977-78 League Cup for us to dispose of which Potteries club?

12. In the same seasons competition we were knocked out by which Midlands club?

13. In which round of the competition did the above game take place?

14. North End disposed of Huddersfield Town by what aggregate score in the 1978-79 competition?

15. Which London club eventually knocked us out of that season's League Cup?

16. By what score did they triumph over us?

17. Birmingham City played in the 1979-80 competition. Can you tell us the aggregate score, was it 0-2, 1-3, or 1-4?

18. What was the furthest round North End got to in the League Cup during the 1970's?

19. North End's highest home League Cup attendance in the 1970's was 28,000 for the visit of which club?

20. Who scored North End's last goal in League Cup in the 1970's?

Answers on page 132

The League Cup 1980's

Another Toughie!

1. Which Midlands club knocked North End out of the 1980-81 League Cup?

2. In an earlier round of the 1980-81 competition North End comfortably disposed of which neighbouring club?

3. We met Halifax Town in the first round of the 1981-82 League Cup, winning the first leg at The Shay 2-1. What was the score in the return leg at Deepdale?

4. The 1979-80 season saw the advent of what in the League Cup?

5. In the 1981-82 competition North End were beaten in the second round by which current Premiership club?

6. And by what aggregate score did they overcome us, was it 4-1, 5-0 or 6-1?

7. Norwich City beat us by what score on aggregate in the 1982-83 League Cup, was it 5-1, 4-1, or 4-2?

8. Which North End player scored twice in the 1982-83 League Cup campaign, was it Steve Elliott, Elliott Ness, or Scott Elliott?

9. In the 1983-84 League Cup we were knocked out in the early stages by which Merseyside club?

10. We narrowly disposed of Tranmere Rovers in the first round of the 1984-85 competition, winning 3-2 at Prenton Park, what was the score in the return leg at Deepdale?

11. In the next round we met which Norfolk Club?

12. The above club eventually beat us by what aggregate score, was it 9-4, 2-1, or 4-3?

13. We scored a famous victory against one of our local rivals in the first round of the 1985-86 League Cup. Name North End's opponents.

14. Try and guess the aggregate score of the above tie. Was it 2-1, 4-1, or 5-2?

15. In the 1986-87 season we were drawn against Blackpool in the first round. What was the score in the first leg tie at Bloomfield Road?

16. You know what's coming next. Tell us the score from the second leg at Deepdale?

17. North End eventually bowed out of the competition in the next round. Who were our conquerors?

18. North End's highest home League Cup attendance in the 1980's was 14,420 for the visit of which Midlands Club?

19. Who scored North End's final League Cup goal of the 1980's?

20. How many times did North End play Blackpool in the League Cup during the 1980's?

Answers on page 132

The League Cup 1990's

We've decided to ease the strain a little by concentrating on more recent League Cup events. Hopefully, you will find this quiz slightly easier or will you?

1. In the 1990-91 League Cup campaign North End were stopped in their tracks in the very first round by which current Third Division Club?

2. Can you tell us the aggregate score in the above tie, was it 5-3, 2-0, or 4-1?

3. We were again beaten in the first round the following season by which Yorkshire side?

4. Once again, can you tell us by what aggregate score North End were beaten by, was it 4-3, 7-6 or 3-2?

5. Which North End player scored in the away leg of the above tie?

6. We beat which Potteries club in the first round first leg tie the following season, 1992-93?

7. What was the eventual aggregate score of the above tie, was it 3-1, 4-1 or 5-2?

8. Which Lancashire club knocked North End out of the League Cup in 1993-94?

9. In the above tie we were beaten 2-1 in the home leg. Who scored North End's goal?

10. And in the away leg we were beaten 4-1. Who scored our solitary goal?

11. We were beaten 5-2 on aggregate against which current First Division club in the 1994-95 League Cup?

12. Who scored our home goal in the home leg of the above tie?

13. And who scored North End's solitary goal in the away leg?

14. Who did we meet in the first round of the 1995-96 League Cup?

15. Can you recall the score from the home leg of that tie?

16. Try and remember the score from the away leg too?

17. A current first team regular scored for North End in that away leg tie. Can you name him?

18. North End's highest home attendance in the League Cup so far in the 1990's (Blackburn 1997 excluded) was 6,323 for the visit of which club?

19. What was the aggregate score when North End beat Rotherham Utd in the League Cup earlier this season?

20. How many times this decade have North End progressed beyond the third round of the League Cup?

Answers on page 132

Goalkeepers (1)

Don't let the questions in this quiz slip through your hands. Judging by the questions there is every chance that you could get slaughtered 20 - 0. Have a go anyway and lets see what the final score is!

1. Name the first black player in English professional football who also kept goal for North End.

2. And in which African country was he born? Was it Nigeria, Zaire or Ghana?

3. In the 'Invincible' era, North End were well served by which international goalkeeper?

4. And what country did he represent?

5. Who was Preston's goalkeeper in the 1888 and 1889 Cup Finals, was it Dr Syntax, Dr Mills-Roberts, or Dr Finlay?

6. How many times was Scottish international keeper Peter McBride capped for his country, was it 6, 42 or 17?

7. Who was the first and undoubtedly the last North End goalkeeper to wear glasses in an FA Cup Final?

8. And against which club was he playing?

9. North End 's goalkeeper Harry Holdcroft kept goal in the 1930s. From which club did we sign him, Everton, Liverpool or Tranmere?

10. How many FA Cup Finals did he play in for Preston?

11. Who succeeded Holdcroft in Preston's goal?

12. In which Irish city was former North End keeper Alan Kelly born?

13. Kelly holds the club record for the most league appearances. Name the figure. Was it 364, 447 or 521?

14. Alan Kelly began his Deepdale career in 1961. In what year did he play his last game for Preston?

15. North End used four goalkeepers during the 1996-97 season. Who made the most League appearances?

16. And who made the least League appearances?

17. Where was Roy Tunks born?

18. In what year did Tunks join the club?

19. Which goalkeeper left Deepdale during the close season?

20. Name the club's current goal keeping coach?

Answers on page 133

Who are we?

Answers on page 152

Can you name this North End player from the past?

Can you also name this North End player from the past?

Crossword (2) answers on page 147

Across

1. North End 'keeper who found success with Newcastle United, winning an FA Cup winners' medal with the Magpies in 1951 (11)

5. Signed from Everton along with Harry Holdcroft (4)

6. North End's South American forward? (6)

8. A 2-1 victory here in 1986-87 clinched promotion (6,6)

9. Brilliant but sometimes erratic goalkeeper (5)

11. Versatile North Ender nicknamed 'Daddy' owing to his sparse locks (4)

13. A tee-totaller, non-smoker and fitness fanatic who appeared in two successive FA Cup Finals in the 1930s (7)

14 and 7 down Industrious right-winger who played for North End before becoming the club's Community Development Officer (5,8)

Down.

1. First switched on in October 1953 (11)

2. Captained the club to the Third Division championship in 1995-96 (3,6)

3. Long-legged winger who later became North End's assistant trainer (7)

4. ..... Farnworth, North End 'keeper (5)

7. See 14 across

10. Defensive stalwart who made 8 League appearances in 1994-95 before joining Scarborough (5)

11. .... Treacy, Republic of Ireland international (3)

12. Number of international caps won by Alex James during his North End days (4)

Tommy Docherty

They threw away the mould when they made Tommy Docherty. These questions encompass Docherty's whole career both as a player and a manager. Let's see how hot you are on the man himself?

1. In which Scottish city was Tommy Docherty born?

2. Which Scottish club did Tommy play for?

3. In what year did he join North End?

4. And how much did it cost us to bring him to Deepdale, was it £4,000, £1,500 or £3,000?

5. He made his North End debut against which Yorkshire club?

6. During that game, Tommy played in which position - right half, inside left, outside left?

7. What was his natural position?

8. Throughout his career, both as a player and manager, his nickname was what?

9. He won the first of his twenty five Scottish caps against which other home country?

10. And in what year did he make his Scottish international debut?

11. After leaving Deepdale, which club did he sign for?

12. How much did North End receive for him, was it £28,000, £16,000 or £24,000?

13. Who was North End's manager at the time of Docherty's departure?

14. After finally hanging up his boots, Docherty became senior coach at which London club?

15. In what year did Docherty return to Deepdale to manage?

16. In what year did he manage Manchester United to FA Cup Final success against Liverpool?

17. In what year was he appointed as Scotland's manager?

18. Which legendary player did Tommy succeed at Deepdale?

19. Name three clubs which he managed.

20. He was sacked from Old Trafford for what reason, was it taking a bung, putting laxative in the opposition's tea, or admitting to an affair with a married woman?

Answers on page 133

Managers

If you're manager of North End the heat is on. Likewise, the heat is on for you in this quiz?

1. North End had 3 different managers in 1981 - can you name them?

2. Who managed North End from 1932 to 1936 and from 1937 to 1949?

3. North End have been managed by 3 members of Man United's European Cup Winning team - who?

4. Which North End manager sold his own son to Liverpool?

5. Which team did John Beck manage before he came to Preston?

6. Alan Ball Snr lost his job as North End manager in 1973 after a 5-0 defeat. Against which team did North End lose?

7. Who was the former Man City player who became North End's manager in April 1985?

8. Bobby Charlton resigned as manager in August 1975 after a dispute over the sale of which player?

9. Who was North End's first post-war manager?

10. Who succeeded Tommy Booth as North End manager?

11. Which former Everton manager was in charge at North End from 1975-77?

12. Who was North End's first full time manager?

13. How many post-war managers have North End had?

14. When North End won the Third Division in 1995/96 how many times was Gary Peters voted Manager of the Month?

15. Which former North End player later managed Torquay Utd., Leicester City and Man Utd.?

16. Which former North End manager played for NASL team San Jose Earthquakes?

17. Which former North End manager played his first game for North End as a player against Leeds in 1949?

18. Who was North End's manager for the 1964 FA Cup Final when North End lost to West Ham?

19. Which manager almost won the First Division twice for North End before resigning after they were relegated in 1961?

20. Who is Assistant Manager to Gary Peters?

Answers on page 133

Tom Finney (1)

North End's greatest ever player with out doubt.

1. What was Finney's nickname?

2. Against which team did Finney make his league debut?

3. How many England caps did Finney win?

4. Finney was voted Footballer of the Year in 1954 and 19??

5. How many league goals did Finney score in 1957/58 when North End finished runners-up in the league?

6. Against which side did Finney hit four goals for England in 1950?

7. How many goals did Finney score for England?

8. How old was Finney when he retired in 1960?

9. In 1954 Finney appeared in the FA Cup Final. North End lost 3-2 to which team?

10. How many league goals did Finney score?

11. Which former team mate said, "If I was pressed into it, I would say that Tom was the best player ever born"?

12. Finney won his only major honour at Club level when North End won Division Two - in which season?

13. In which season was The Tom Finney Stand opened?

14. Finney won his last two England caps in 1959 - against which two sides?

15. In what year was Tom Finney born?

16. Finney's farewell appearance was at Deepdale at the end of the 1959/60 season - against which team?

17. How many league games did Finney play in for North End?

18. Finney appeared in 40 FA Cup ties for North End. How many goals did he score?

19. How many times did Finney play alongside Stanley Mathews for England?

20. How many league hat-tricks did Finney score?

Answers on page 134

Backroom Staff

If you know your North End this is as easy as beating Blackpool! honest.

1. Which three clubs did physio Mick Rathbone play for?

2. Name North End's Chief Scout.

3. Who did Geoff McDougal succeed as North End's Youth Development Officer?

4. Name the club which Mick Rathbone managed for a spell?

5. How many first team appearances did Kelham O'Hanlon make last season?

6. Which club did Neil McDonald sign from?

7. In what month did Neil McDonald become a Youth Team Coach at Deepdale?

8. At which club did Steve Harrison begin his playing career?

9. Which Canadian club did Steve Harrison play for?

10. Which member of the back room staff was voted Player of the Year last season?

11. In what year did Gary Peters become a professional soccer player?

12. Name North End's Head Groundsman? Is it Peter O'Toole, Peter Cushing or Peter McCallion?

13. In what year did Steve Harrison join North End?

14. In what competition did Neil McDonald make his debut for North End?

15. Name the three previous clubs which Chief Scout Alan Fogarty has worked for?

16. Who is North End's new Cheif Executive?

17. In what year was Gary Peters appointed manager at North End?

18. At which club did Steve Harrison end his playing career?

19. At which club did Neil McDonald begin his playing career?

20. Who has just been appointed full-time coach for Lancashire Lynx?

Answers on page 134

Present Strikers

You should be bang on target here!

1. In what Lancashire town was Lee Cartwright born?

2. Which club was Michael Holt a trainee with before joining North End?

3. Against which club did Jonathan Macken score his debut goal for North End?

4. How many goals did Kurt Nogan score for Burnley in the 1995-96 season?

5. How much did North End pay the Clarets for Nogan; £100,000, £150,000 or £175,000?

6. Against which club did David Reeves make his North End debut?

7. David Reeves was top scorer last season. With how many goals?

8. Who scored North End's two goals in the home victory against Watford this season?

9. Kurt Nogan has been capped at U/21 level for which country?

10. Which Man Utd player did Jonathan Macken say he learnt the most from?

11. Which team did striker Michael Holt support as a boy, Leeds,

Celtic or Blackburn?

12. Which team did Lee Cartwright play against in his 'comeback' game last season?

13. In what year did Lee Cartwright sign professional forms with the club?

14. Against which team did Lee Ashcroft pick up a hamstring injury last season?

15. In which town was David Reeves born?

16. And what Yorkshire City does David Reeves now live in?

17. How many league cup goals did Michael Holt score last season?

18. Name Jonathan Macken's favourite film - Die Hard II, Braveheart or Superman?

19. Apart from football which other sport does Jonathan Macken enjoy - fly fishing, topless darts or tennis?

20. Name Kurt Nogan's favourite hobby, is it, wrestling, gambling or Knitting?

Answers on page 134

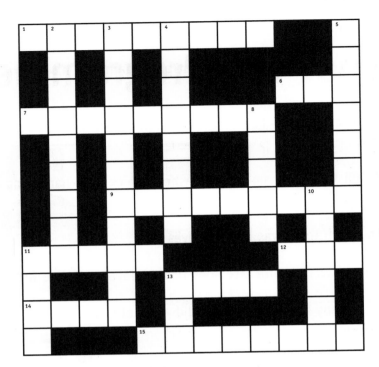

Crossword (3) answers on 148

Across

1. North End 'keeper who began his career with Bolton Wanderers (9)

6. .... O'Riordan, versatile North Ender (3)

7. North End manager who reached the pinnacle of his success with Everton in the 1960s and 70s (9)

9. The club's leading goalscorer in 1974-75 (3,6)

11. Former Burnley player who managed the Lilywhites from 1968 to 1970 (5)

12. Number of shirt worn by George Ross (3)

13. Half-back who made 212 League appearances between 1903 and 1911 (4)

14. .... Spavin, who served Preston for 12 seasons (4)

15. The scorer of North End's first-ever League goal (8)

Down.

2. Former North End defender who also had a spell as youth team coach and caretaker-manager (9)

3. Team that pipped North End for the Fourth Division championship in 1986-87 (11)

4. Signed from West Ham United, he played in 129 League and Cup games before later finding fame as a manager (8)

5. England winger who scored for North End after just seven seconds against Manchester City in 1949 (7)

8. Father and son goalkeepers (5)

10. It's in the ref's whistles (6)

11. Signed from Stoke City for £70,000 in July 1989 (4)

13. Replaced Tommy Docherty as Preston manager (3)

Spot the Programme

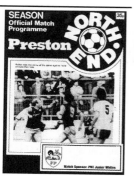

Simply tell us the
season in which you
think these eight
programmes
were issued.

**Answers on
page 152**

North End lost the 1964 F.A. Cup Final against West Ham, 2-3.
Fill in the team sheet for the game and the scorers

Answers on page 152

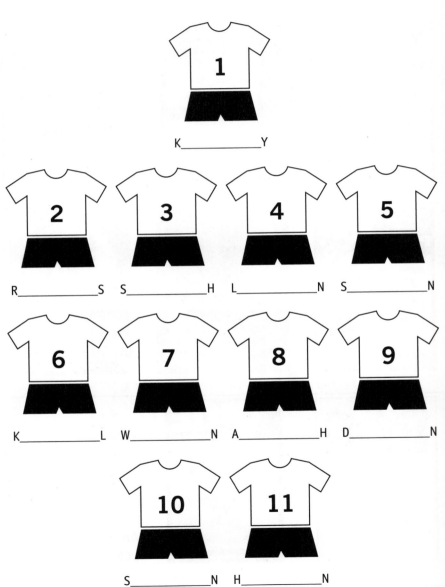

Who are we?

Answers on page 152

This former player is still playing in the North West. Who is he?

Name this North End player in action.

FA Cup Finals

We decided to dispense with the obligatory twenty questions in this quiz; prefering instead to concentrate on quality rather than quantity. Let's see how you got on anyway.

Preston North End have appeared in seven FA Cup Finals. What you have to do is name the opponents and the final score. Simple isn't it?

Year	Opponents	Score
1888		
1889		
1922		
1937		
1938		
1954		
1964		

To test your knowledge of North End even further, here are some more questions concerning the FA Cup.

1. In what year did North End first participate in the FA Cup?

2. And who were their first opponents?

3. What is North End's record score in the FA Cup, is it 24-0, 25-0 or 26-0?

4. Against which side did they record that historic scoreline, was it a boys team, Hasslingdon or Hyde?

5. Who opened the scoring for North End in the 1889 final against Wolves?

6. Who opened the scoring for North End in the 1937 final against Sunderland?

7. In the 1954 final against West Bromwich Albion, who equalised for North End just a minute after the Baggies had taken a 20th minute lead?

8. Who scored the opening goal for North End in the 1964 final?

9. What division were Preston in when we contested the 1964 final against West Ham?

10. Which player was dropped in favour of Howard Kendall in the same game?

Answers on page 135

FA Cup 1970's

In this quiz, we test your knowledge of North End's progress in the FA Cup during the 1970s. We'll be asking you to name teams, scorers and scores in various FA Cup ties involving our club. Let's get started.

1. In 1971-72 North End were eliminated from the competition in the fourth round, by which First Division (old style) club?

2. In the third round of the competition, we had beaten which club 4-2?

3. Which current Second Division club knocked North End out of the competition after a replay in 1972-73?

4. Which London club knocked us out in the third round the following season?

5. In the 1974-75 season, North End were knocked out of the competition by which Cumbrian club?

6. We were knocked out of the competition at the second round stage in 1975-76 by Scarborough. By what score did they beat us?

7. In 1976-77 we were engaged in an epic struggle which eventually went to a third game. Who were North End's opponents?

8. In relation to the above match, the second replay was eventually played at which ground?

9. We were eventually knocked out of that year's competition by which Yorkshire club?

10. In the 1977-78 season, we made it to which round?

11. In 1978-79 we were knocked out of the competition at the fourth round stage by Southampton. Who did we overcome in the third round?

12. In the 1974-75 competition, we played a famous North East non-league club in the first round. Can you name them?

13. In the same season's competition, we came up against one of Bob Paisley's former clubs in the second round. Can you name them?

14. In the above game, a former Manchester United legend scored for North End. Can you name him?

15. Who scored twice for North End in the third round of the competition in 1978-79?

16. North End's highest FA Cup attendance during the 1970s was 37,052 for the visit of which club?

17. In 1977-78 we beat which club in the first round of the competition?

18. Name one of the goalscorers for North End in the above game.

19. How many FA Cup games involving North End were played at Deepdale during the 1970s, was it 11, 15 or 9?

20. During the 1970s we never managed to get past which round of the competition?

Answers on page 135

FA Cup 1980's

1. In 1979-80 we were knocked out of the competition by which East Anglian club?

2. The following season, Bristol Rovers knocked us out in the third round at Deepdale. What was the score?

3. In the 1981-82 season, Chesterfield beat North End 4-1 in the first round. Who scored our goal?

4. In the first round of the 1982-83 competition, which non-league club did we beat?

5. Which local rivals did we beat 2-1 at home in the same season's competition?

6. In the same season, we eventually made it to the third round of the competition where we were beaten 3-0 by which Yorkshire club?

7. Which round did North End make it to in 1983-84?

8. Which part-timers club beat us 4-1 in the competition in 1984-85?

9. In the previous round of the FA Cup, we had triumphed 4-3 at Deepdale against which Lancashire club?

10. Preston were knocked out by a Midlands club in 1985-86. Can you name them?

11. There was a remarkable scoreline in the above match, was it? 9-6, 7-3 or 6-2?

12. In the 1986-87 competition, North End were drawn to play away at Chorley. Where was the game actually played?

13. The above game eventually went to a replay, which North End won by how many goals?

14. Having survived the might of Chorley, we were drawn against which North East club in the next round?

15. North End eventually made it to the fourth round of that season's competition when we were knocked out by Newcastle United. By what score did they beat us?

16. In the 1987-88 competition, which round were we knocked out in?

17. Which Merseyside club were we drawn against in the 1988-89 competition?

18. In the above game we drew the home game 1-1 only to succumb to what score in the replay, was it 4-1, 5-1 or 3-0?

19. North End's highest FA Cup attendance during the 1980s was 16,986 for the visit of which club?

20. In the 1980s how many times did we make it to the fourth round of the FA Cup?

Answers on page 135

FA Cup 1990's

1. In the 1989-90 season, which Merseyside club did we beat 1-0 in the early stages of the competition?

2. In the above match, who scored the decisive goal for North End?

3. In the same season we were knocked out of the competition by which non-league club?

4. By what score did Mansfield Town beat us in the 1990-91 competition?

5. The following season saw our tie away to Mansfield Town abandoned after 32 minutes because of what, a streaker, foodlight failure or fog?

6. What was the score when the referee abandoned the above match?

7. In the re-scheduled match, North End eventually won 1-0. Who scored the goal?

8. In the same season's competition we were eventually knocked out at the third round stage by which South Yorkshire club?

9. Bradford City knocked us out at the first round stage in 1992-93. By what score did they beat us, was it 2-1, 4-0 or 5-4?

10. During our 1993-94 FA Cup campaign, we met Bournemouth in the third round. We won the tie 2-1 at Deepdale, but can you name the current member of the back room staff who scored that day?

11. In the same season's competition we were eventually beaten in the fourth round by which non-league club?

12. What was the score in the above encounter?

13. In 1994-95 we met arch-rivals Blackpool in the first round at Deepdale. What was the score?

14. Name the crowd figure for the above match. Was it 16,427, 9,602, 14,036?

15., In the next round of the same season's competition, we were knocked out by which Midlands club?

16. Which round did we make it to in 1995-96?

17. And who eventually knocked us out of the competition?

18. North End's highest FA Cup attendance so far in the 1990s was 14,337 for the visit of which Yorkshire club?

19. What is the furthest North End have been in the competition during the 1990s?

20. Who knocked North End out of the FA Cup in 1996-97?

Answers on page 136

FA Cup Semi-Finals

Preston North End have participated in ten FA Cup Semi Finals up to the end of the 1996-97 season. The following twenty questions will test your knowledge of their opponents in those games as well as your skill in identifying the venue the games were played at.

Date	Score
5th Match 1887	**1-3**

1. (a) Opponents
   (b) Venue

18th February 1888	**4-0**

2. (a) Opponents
   (b) Venue

16th March 1889	**1-0**

3. (a) Opponents
   (b) Venue

4th March 1893	**2-2**

4. (a) Opponents
   (b) Venue

16th March 1893	**0-0**

5. (a) Opponents
   (b) Venue

20th March 1893	**1-2**

6. (a) Opponents
   (b) Venue

19th March 1921   1-2

7. (a) Opponents
   (b) Venue

25th March 1922   2-1

8. (a) Opponents
   (b) Venue

10th April 1937   4-1

9. (a) Opponents
   (b) Venue

26th March 1938   2-1

10. (a) Opponents
    (b) Venue

27th March 1954   2-0

11. (a) Opponents
    (b) Venue

14th March 1964   2-1

12. (a) Opponents
    (b) Venue

Answers on page 136

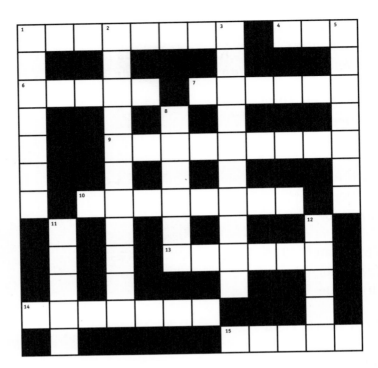

Crossword (4) answers on page 148

Across

1. England Under-21 international who returned to Deepdale for a second spell from West Bromwich Albion (8)

4. .... Dagger, North End winger of the late 1950s (3)

6. Bright wing-half of the 1960s ! (5)

7. England international who later helped Liverpool win the Second Division championship (6)

9. North End's last ....opponents in the FA Cup were Kidderminster Harriers (3,6)

10. Rejected by North End in 1956, he became one of Blackpool's most prolific scorers before returning to Deepdale (8)

13. Former Hull City right-back who playd in 43 League games in the mid 1980s (6)

14. First Australian-born player to be selected for the Football League XI (7)

15. Manager who sold his son to Liverpool (5)

Down.

1. Team that beat North End 2-1 in the FA Charity Shield match of 1938 (7)

2. Celebrated amateur team that provided North End with some classic encounters (11)

3. Captained North End in the 1937 FA Cup Final (10)

5. Moses ...., a robust player who started his career with the Black Knights (7)

8. Scored a hat-trick against Reading in 1970-71 and finished the season as the top scorer (6)

11. Young North End 'keeper (5)

12. Joined North End from Norwich City for 125,000 - at the time, the club's most expensive player (5)

The Third Division Championship was decided with a 3-0 win over Rotherham in May 1971.
Fill in the team sheet for the game and the scorers

Answers on page 152

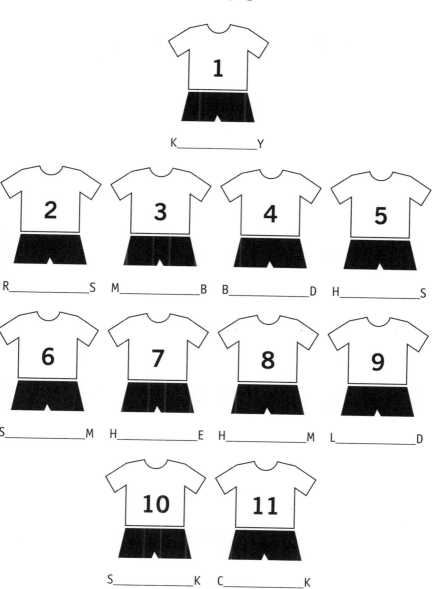

1 K_____Y

2 R_____S   3 M_____B   4 B_____D   5 H_____S

6 S_____M   7 H_____E   8 H_____M   9 L_____D

10 S_____K   11 C_____K

Penalties

This quiz will put you on the spot instead of the player. Let's see if you've got the bottle in this sudden death quiz.

1. Who scored North End's first ever penalty?

2. And who were North End playing on that fateful day?

3. In what year did Deepdale keeper Peter McBride fake a penalty, only to miss it, was it 1904, 1901 or 1917?

4. And against which Midlands club were North End playing that day?

5. Which player missed from the spot twice in the opening three games of the 1934-35 season?

6. Which player took over from Pears as the club's main penalty taker during the following season?

7. What was so controversial about the penalty awarded against North End in the 1922 FA Cup Final against Huddersfield Town?

8 Who was Preston's goalkeeper in that game?

9. George Mutch, the penalty hero of the 1938 FA Cup Final was born in which Scottish city?

10. In that game, North End got the winner in which minute of the game, was it 89, 92 or 120?

11. And which Yorkshire club were they playing against?

12. Preston's opponents in the 1954 FA Cup Final were awarded a penalty - name the opposition.

13. Who was North End's goalkeeper that day?

14. Name the North End player who gave away the penalty.

15. What is the new rule concerning penalties which has been introduced for the 1997-98 season?

16. In the 1954 FA Cup Final what was unusual about the penalty goal scored against North End?

17. In what year did North End gain their first ever penalty, was it 1842, 1926 or 1891?

18. When North End were awarded a penalty in the 1938 FA Cup Final, what was the score before the kick was taken?

19. Name the opposition goalkeeper in that game. Was it Beresford, Shearer or Hesford?

20. During the Championship winning season of 1995-96, who scored North End's first penalty?

Answers on page 136

Bill Shankly

No North End quiz would be complete without some questions on the late, great Bill Shankly. Let us test your knowledge with these questions.

1. How much did North End pay Carlisle United for Bill Shankly's signature? £67, £1,000, £500?

2. In what year did Shankly pick up an FA Cup winners medal with North End?

3. How many appearances did he make in his first full season at North End? 25, 17, 32?

4. How many times did Shankly miss a game through injury? 28, 9, 1?

5. In what season did he make his league debut with Carlisle United?

6. What was his favourite brand of tea? Tetley tea bags, herbal tea or Typhoo tea?

7. His first managerial post came at which club?

8. In what year did he become Liverpool's manager?

9. How tall was Bill Shankly? 5ft 7ins, 5ft 4ins, 5ft 10ins?

10. In what year did Shankly die?

11. In what year did Shankly become North End's Reserves player/coach?

12. How many full Scottish international caps did he win? 10, 22, 5?

13. In what year did Bill Shankly first win the FA Cup for Liverpool?

14. Name the last club he managed before moving to Anfield?

15. How many league games did he play for North End, was it 312, 296 or 282?

16. In his first full season at Deepdale, Shankly helped North End to promotion to which division?

17. In what year did Bill Shankly resign as manager of Liverpool?

18. Who did Shankly succeed as Huddersfield Town manager?

19. Who was Bill's favourite boxer?

20. How many First Division Championships did Liverpool win under Bill Shankly, was it 3, 4 or 5?

Answers on page 137

The 1950's

1. In what year did Tom Finney get his last cap?

2. North End finished league runners-up twice in the 1950's - which years?

3. Which Lancashire team lost to Arsenal depriving North End of the 1952/53 First Division title?

4. In which season did North End win the Second Division?

5. An ever present in the 1950/51 season, he later joined Carlisle who is he?

6. In what year did North End sign Jimmy Baxter from Barnsley, was it 1950, 1952 or 1954?

7. In what season did North End score 100 goals?

8. North End had only four managers in the 1950s - who?

9. Which Preston player played left wing in the 1958 FA Cup Final?

10. Who made his North End debut at Old Trafford in September 1953?

11. Who made his debut due to the absences of Tommy Docherty and Frank O'Farrell in August 1958?

12. Who was the Australian born player who joined North End in

October 1950?

13. Who was the former Derby County forward, who had nine years at Deepdale before going to Millwall?

14. Who was manager Cliff Britton's first signing as manager? This player later went on to non-league Weymouth as player manager.

15. In 1952 an Italian club tried to sign Tom Finney for a £10,000 signing-on fee, a car and a villa. Which club?

16. Which Scottish born player made 440 league appearances for North End, mainly in the 1950s?

17. Who made his debut in 1954 but did not replace George Thompson as first choice keeper until 1956/57?

18. Which team did North End lose to in the 1954 FA Cup Final?

19. Which team did North End beat in the 1954 FA Cup Semi-Final, was it Manchester United, Sheffield Wednesday or Arsenal?

20. In 1958 North End had their biggest overseas victory against Border FC. Which country do they play in, Isle of Man, South Africa or The Falklands?

Answers on page 137

Transfers

Money talks in football - North End have been involved with transfer of some famous names. How much of a wheeler dealer are you?

1. Allan Smart was signed from which Scottish club in November 1994?

2. Graham Lancashire was also signed in 1994 from neighbours Burnley. For how much?

3. Who is North End's record signing?

4. North End broke the then British transfer record in December 1949, when they paid £26,000 for whom?

5. North End's record transfer receipts came from the sale of Kevin Kilbane to WBA. Prior to that came when Manchester City bought which player?

6. Gerry Ingram was signed from Blackpool but to which club did North End eventually sell him?

7. Leyton Orient signed this popular player in 1972?

8. Who were Bobby Charlton's first signings as manager?

9. Which club did Lee Ashcroft sign for before rejoining North End?

10. Which club did Gary Bennett join last season after

leaving Deepdale?

11. Steve Wilkinson joined Chesterfield in the summer, but from which club did North End sign the popular striker?

12. Which player did Les Chapman sell to Sheffield United?

13. Lincoln City sold a former North End star to Port Vale in September 97. North End received 25% of the fee. Who was the player?

14. Bobby Mimms signed for Rotherham United after leaving North End. What was the fee?

15. Which team did Mark Lawrenson sign for in July 1971?

16. Which prolific goal scorer was signed by North End from Oldham for £20,000 in 1987?

17. Another former Oldham player who signed for North End via Norwich in December 1990 for £125,000?

18. Dean Barrick was signed from Cambridge United in September 1995. Which North End player went in the opposite direction as part of the deal?

19. Which former Bolton, Coventry and WBA player joined North End as part of the deal that saw Kevin Kilbane go to the Hawthornes?

20. Micky Brown rejoined one of his former clubs midway through last season - which club, was it, Shrewsbury, West Ham or Orient?

Answers on page 137

Football Anagrams

Who are these mixed up football stars past and present.

1. EEORG STBE

2. AALN RSAHERE

3. VIDAD AESMNE

4. ELPE

5. ELGN DODLEH

6. MIJMY VREAGES

7. SEL ERFDNINDA

8. YNNEK LSHILADG

9. VDAID CKHABEM

10. BBBYO ROOME

11. ZGZAA

12. LOZA

13. KRMA RALWNSEON

14. ACJK RLCTHNOA

15. YANND LCFBAHNOREWL

16. TASNEYL TAHMTWES

17. NGODRO KABNS

18. RAGY NIKELRE

19. REPET HTOLSIN

20. VTRERO KROONGIB

Answers on page 138

Crossword (5) answers on page 149

Across

1. Beaten 9-0 by North End in May 1966 (7,4)

6. He once scored four first-half goals against Queen's Park Rangers (6)

7. Number worn by 5 down in the 1964 FA Cup Final (4)

8. Scored eight of North End's goals in the 26-0 FA Cup win over Hyde (4)

9.and 13 down German-born North End 'keeper (3,5)

11. Number worn by Fred Else amongst others (3)

12. Preston-born forward who later played for Bury and Barrow (6)

14. Ball-playing midfielder who left for Millwall in the summer of 1991 (5)

15. Number of goals scored by North End when they played Stoke in 1889 (3)

16. Gary Brazil scored in both matches against this side in 1987-88 (4)

17. Signed from Oldham Athletic for 80,000 in March 1979 (4)

18. The club's only ever-present in 1989-90 (5)

Down

1. Arriving midway through the 1921-22 season from Glenbuck Cherrypickers, he played in 392 League games before leaving to join Blackpool (8)

2. Weapon-named outside-right of the 1950s (6)

3. Finney, Dawson and Mutch were all ....(8)

4. Peter or Tommy (8)

5. Centre-half in North End's FA Cup Final team of 1964 (9)

10. Influential midfielder who was a member of the 1995-96 PFA award winning third division team (5)

13. See 9 across

14. .... Kelly, England international signed from Burnley in 1932 (3)

In 1987 North End won promotion from Division Four with a 2-1 win over Orient
Fill in the team sheet for the game and the scorers and sub

Answers on page 152

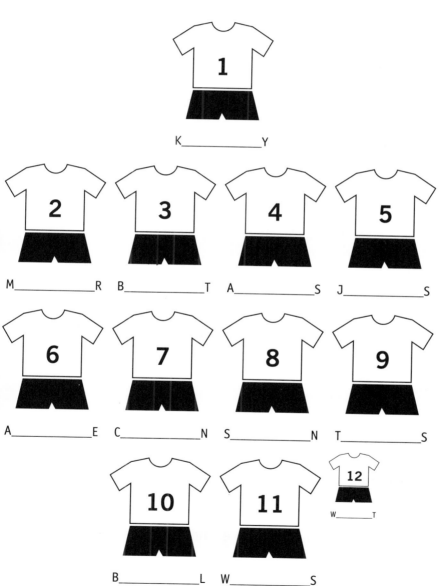

1 — K_____Y

2 — M_____R

3 — B_____T

4 — A_____S

5 — J_____S

6 — A_____E

7 — C_____N

8 — S_____N

9 — T_____S

10 — B_____L

11 — W_____S

12 — W____T

Gary Peters

He's the man in charge - but what do you know about him? Here's your chance to show us... be warned, there are some tricky questions to keep you on your toes.

1. How old is Gary Peters (October 1997)?

2. Who did Gary Peters succeed as manager of North End?

3. Which now defunct club did Gary Peters play league football for?

4. How many FA Cup Finals did he play in?

5. How many league appearances did Gary Peters make as a player? 381, 431, 481?

6. Gary Peters played for four different clubs. Name them?

7. Gary Peters played for two clubs in two different spells, which clubs?

8. Gary Peters was assistant to John Beck at which club before they both joined North End?

9. How many league goals did Gary Peters score in his career as a player (to the nearest ten)?

10. As a player, how many times did Gary Peters win promotion?

11. Which team did North End play for Gary Peters first game as manager, and what was the score?

12. North End's first victory under Gary's management was against which team?

13. Has Gary ever made a league appearance for Preston?

14. Who was the first player that Gary Peters signed for North End?

15. How many other clubs has Gary been manager of?

16. How many times was Gary, Manager of the Month in North End's promotion season?

17. How many times was Gary, Manager of the Month last season?

18. How many international caps did Gary win as a player?

19. What was Gary's first club?

20. What position did North End finish in Gary's first season in charge?

Answers on page 138

Goalkeepers (2)

Over the years North End have had some exceptional 'Keepers' including current stars "Tepi" and David Lucas. Can we catch you out on them and their predecessors.

1. David Lucas played in the 1997 U21 World Cup for England, where was the tournament held?

2. Which 'keeper was known as Handsome Harry and kept goal for North End at the only 17 years of age?

3. In what season did Alan Kelly Snr make his North End debut?

4. Alan Kelly Snr played his last game for North End after injuring his shoulder against which team?

5. Alan Kelly Snr has two sons who play professional football, both as 'keeper. Who are they and who do they play for (Oct 97)?

6. Who played in goal in the last ever game on the plastic - was it Steve Woods, Alan Kelly Snr or Kelham O'Hanlon?

7. When John Vaughan left North End which club did he join?

8. Former North End 'keeper Bobby Mimms played in an Merseyside FA Cup Final when at Everton. In which year?

9. Which club did Bobby Mimms join in summer 1997?

10. From which Scottish club did Kelham O'Hanlon re-join North End in 1996?

11. Who was North End manager when popular 'keeper Roy Tunks left North End?

12. How many league games did Tunks play for North End; 380, 480 or 580?

13. Fred Else joined another Lancashire team from North End and played against North End as the day of his transfer. Which team was it?

14. For which country was Kelham O'Hanlon capped?

15. Which country does Tepi play in goal for?

16. XXXXXX were knocked out of the 1998 World Cup due to a bizarre last minute goal scored against 'Tepi' - What happened?

17. Alan Kelly Jnr made his debut in 1985/86 against which team?

18. In what year was 'Tepi' born? Was it 1972, 1973, 1974?

19. Who was the last 'keeper to manage North End?

20. Who started in goal in the 1994/95 season?

Answers on page 138

General Football

In this quiz we will be asking you twenty questions concerning football generally. Let's see how you get on. They are easy!

1. Who won this season's Charity Shield (1997-98)?

2. Which football league side are nicknamed the Robins?

3. Where is the 1998 World Cup being held?

4. Which current Premiership manager got a one year ban for taking bungs?

5. Which former Middlesborough player now plays for Athletico Madrid?

6. Who did Liverpool sign Paul Ince from?

7. How many times has Howard Kendall managed Everton?

8. Which former Southampton player now trains race horses?

9. Which former Man City and Derby player also trains race horses?

10. How many times have Liverpool won the European Cup?

11. Which Second Division club reached last season's FA Cup Semi Final?

12. Who won the FA Cup in 1970?

13. Name Tranmere Rover's current manager.

14. Who became England's manager after Walter Winterbottom?

15. Who won the FA Cup in 1968?

16. Who did Manchester United beat in the 1968 European Cup final?

17. In which city did Celtic win the European Cup in 1967?

18. Which country finished second in England's qualifing group for the 1998 World Cup?

19. Who won the Coca Cola Cup in 1994-95?

20. Where was the 1958 World Cup tournament held?

Answers on page 139

Honours

North End have plenty of silverware in their trophy cabinet. Unfortunately, some of it is that old your grandmother could have polished it!

1. Why couldn't North End try to retain the Marsden Cup they won in 1996?

2. North End were the first team to win the 'double' - four other sides have since completed the 'double', which four?

3. Which team did North End beat in the 1964 FA Cup semi final?

4. How many times have North End appeared in the Charity Shield?

5. North End have been Division 1 runners-up six times - when was the last one?

6. How many times have North End been beaten FA Cup finalists?

7. In 1952/53, when North End were runners-up in the First Division, which team were Champions?

8. North End won a war-time Cup Final, in which year?

9. Which team beat North End in the 1964 FA Cup Final?

10. North End reached Wembley in the 1993/94 play-offs, which team did they lose to?

11. In the 1994-95 play-offs, North End lost over two legs to which current First Division side?

12. Which current North End players were in the 2nd Division PFA team for 1996/97?

13. When North End won the 1889 FA Cup, who did they beat in the final?

14. Where were the 1888 and 1889 FA Cup finals played?

15. North End won the Third Division in 1970-71. How many points (2 for a win) did they get? 58, 61, 64?

16. North End were involved in the first ever televised FA Cup final - in what year?

17. In which year did North End reach the final of the FA Youth Cup? (Clue: Alan Spavin and Peter Thompson were in the team).

18. North End created a record by winning how many consecutive games? 32, 42, 52?

19. When did North End last reach the third round of the FA Cup?

20. When did North End last beat a Premiership side in a competition?

Answers on page 139

Anagrams

In this particular quiz the names of various current North End players and staff have been jumbled up. Can you identify the names?

1. LIMHEAC SONJACK

2. TURK NAGON

3. ANES GANERG

4. EEL FORTSACH

5. VIDAD SEERVE

6. RAGY NIKSONRAP

7. LINCO COKDRUM

8. VIDAD YESMO

9. VOTUE LIMONEAN

10. RANY DIKD

11. JEMIA RISQUES

12. VADID CULSA

13. LIMHEAC THOL

14. RAGY SETPER

15. EEL RITRACWTHG

16. HAMLEK LOONHAN

17. ALUP NEKMANC

19. NEAD RICKBAR

20. LIMHEAC NOTLEPAP

Answers on page 139

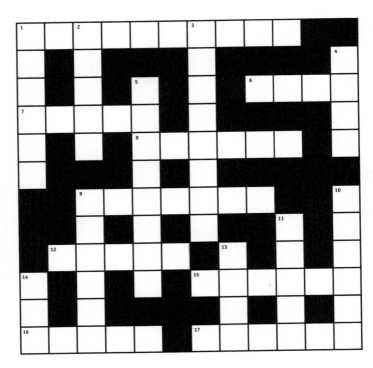

Crossword (6) answers on page 149

Across

1. Scored the only goal at Southampton in the last match of 1933-34 to put Preston back in the First Division (10)

6. Beaten 26-0 in a first round FA Cup tie (4)

7. Former idol of North End fans now with Blackpool (5)

8. Hong Kong-born forward who played in just seven games in the 1980s (6)

9. John Thomas hit a hat-trick against this local non-League side in the FA Cup competition of 1986-87 (6)

12. Percy ......,who ended his first season, 1902-03 as the club's top scorer (5)

15. Captain of North End's 1964 FA Cup Final side (6)

16. Former Sunderland wing-half who played in 224 League games for North End (5)

17. The Preston Plumber (6)

Down

1. Present North End manager (6)

2. Midfielder signed from Raith Rovers in 1966 (5)

3. Brothers Frank and Hugh (8)

4. North End manager renowned for a 'direct style'! (4)

5. Former Northampton Town forward who formed a good partnership with Alex Dawson (8)

9. Former Middlesbrough player, for whom they paid out the first four-figure transfer for his services - North End bought him from Woolwich Arsenal (6)

10. Dublin-born midfielder who scored 20 goals in 128 League games before joining Sunderland (6)

11. Neil Young scored both goals against this team in a 2-2 draw at Deepdale in November 1973 (5)

13. North End's sponsors (4)

14. He scored in his first four games for the club and whenever he scored, North End never lost ! (3)

Tom Finney's last game was against Luton Town in 1960
Fill in the team sheet for the game and the scorers

Answers on page 152

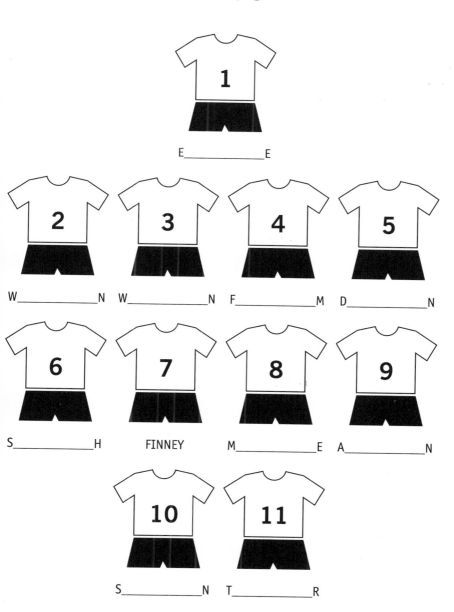

1

E_____E

2

W_____N

3

W_____N

4

F_____M

5

D_____N

6

S_____H

7

FINNEY

8

M_____E

9

A_____N

10

S_____N

11

T_____R

Current defenders

A watertight defence is the key to success. See how watertight you are on your North End back line.

1. Which team did Colin Murdock make his North End league debut against?

2. Name the town in Northern Ireland where Colin Murdock was born?

3. Which club did North End sign Tepi from?

4. Which club did Deepdale defender Ryan Kidd begin his career with?

5. What was Dean Barrick's previous club?

6. How much did North End pay Bury for Michael Jackson?

7. Against which team did Sean Gregan score his debut goal for North End?

8. Against which club did Dean Barrick make his debut for North End?

9. In what year did Jamie Squires sign professional forms with the club?

10. Which club did we sign Paul Sparrow from?

11. Which other award did Gary Parkinson win last season other than being voted in the PFA Division Two team?

12. Name Gary Parkinson's three previous clubs?

13. Which defender scored at Chesterfield this season?

14. In which Lancashire town was Ryan Kidd born?

15. Which club did David Lucas go on loan to last season?

16. Which club did Michael Jackson make his North End debut against?

17. How many games did Sean Gregan play for Preston last season?

18. How tall is Teuvo Moilanen?

19. Name the five professional clubs which North End goalkeeping coach Kelham O'Hanlon played for?

20. Which defender was substitute for the first two games this season?

Answers on page 140

League Grounds

In this quiz we want you to identify the name of the club from the ground in which they play. Couldn't be simpler, or could it?

1. Ashton Gate

2. The Dell

3. Prenton Park

4. Plainmore

5. Spotland

6. Brisbane Road

7. Highfield Road

8. Fratton Park

9. London Road

10. County Ground

11. Elm Park

12. Bramall Lane

13. Glanford Park

14. Gay Meadow

15. Upton Park

16. Loftus Road

17. Edgeley Park

18. Vetch Field

19. Sincil Bank

20. Filbert Street

Answers on page 140

1997/98 Division Two Opposition

If you are a true Northender you'll need to know about our opposition - this quiz will test just how much 'scouting' you need to do!

1. Which team was saved from the receivers by the fans last year?

2. Which of the two Bristol clubs play on a Rugby ground?

3. Which London club is Kevin Keegan now at the helm of?

4. Which team did North End beat in front of SKY cameras in October?

5. How many London teams do North End play in the league this season?

6. How many Lancashire derbies in the league will North End play this season?

7. There is only one Derbyshire side in Division Two this season - who?

8. Which team plays furthest from Deepdale?

9. Which is the most westerly based team North End will meet in the league this season?

10. Which is the most easterly based team North End will meet in the league this season?

11. Which team are managed by a former England manager?

12. Who started the season as Oldham's manager?

13. Which club chairman took over team selection after sacking Mervyn Day?

14. Which team signed French soccer star Roger Boli?

15. Where do Wycombe Wanderers play?

16. Where do York City play?

17. Which team play at Saltergate?

18. Which ground is nearer to Deepdale? Blackpool or Burnley?

19. Where will Wigan play next year?

20. Which club is having a new National Football Museum built?

Answers on page 140

Internationals

1. Who was the last North End player (Oct 97) to receive a full international cap?

2. Tom Finney is North End's most capped player. How many caps did he win?

3. Other than Tom Finney, who was the last North End player (whilst still at Deepdale) to win a full cap for England?

4. After Tom Finney, who is North End's second most capped player?

5. How many caps did Mark Lawrenson receive for the Republic of Ireland whilst a North End player?

6. Lee Ashcroft has been capped by England at U21 level - how many times?

7. Against which country did Tom Finney make his international debut?

8. How many full caps did Alan Kelly jnr win whilst at North End?

9. Who was the last North End manager to manage an international side?

10. Who were the first North End players to be capped? (Clue: they played in the same game!)

11. What was the last international football match to be staged at Deepdale?

12. How many international goals did Tom Finney score?

13. Which representative side did North End play in summer 1997?

14. Willie Irvine was capped three times in the 1969 season. For which country?

15. How many Scottish caps did Bill Shankly win whilst at North End? 5, 15 or 25?

16. How many times did Alan Kelly Snr play in an international v England?

17. Who was the first Preston player to be capped by the Republic of Ireland? (He later went on to manage Manchester United)

18. How many caps did Bobby Charlton win whilst a North End player?

19. Which North End player made three appearances for Wales in 1964 and 65?

20. For which country did Kevin Kilbane get an international call-up before he went to WBA?

Answers on page 141

Local Rivals

In this quiz we want you to identify the team which has been omitted. We have already given you the name of one team. All you have to do is to identify that team's local rival.

1. Manchester United v

2. AC Milan v

3. Everton v

4. Lazio v

5. Sunderland v

6. Hibernian v

7. Rangers v

8. Sheffield United v

9. Blackpool v

10. Tranmere Rovers v

11. Ajax v

12. Arsenal v

13. Leicester City v

14. Aston Villa v

15. Bristol Rovers v

16. Fulham v

17. Nottingham Forest v

18. Southampton v

19. Ipswich Town v

20. Watford v

Answers on page 141

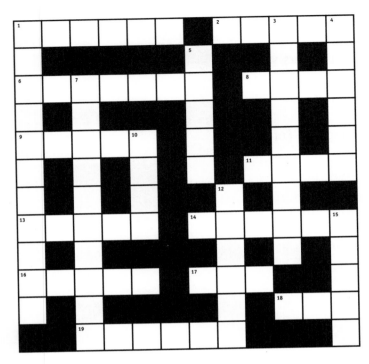

Crossword (7) answers on page 150

Across

1. Northern Ireland international who scored a hat-trick against Huddersfield Town in only his second game (6)

2. Experienced 'keeper who played for Everton, Spurs and Blackburn Rovers before joining North End (5)

6. North End's record League ......is 10-0 against Stoke (7)

8. Central defender signed from Doncaster Rovers in March 1967 who went on to appear in 166 League games for Preston (4)

9. Direction Preston are going? (5)

11. Charlie Wayman scored this number of goals in the first half of a match against Queen's Park Rangers on Christmas Day(4)

13. Former North Ender in charge of the club's successful youth side of 1960 (5)

14. Former Manchester United and England midfielder who became Preston manager in July 1977 (6)

16. Jimmy Ross scored ..... goals when North End beat Hyde 26-0 (5)

17. Popular name for Dunblane-born striker

....Napier who played one League game for North End in 1963-64 (3)

18. .... Beresford, signed from Aston Villa (3)

19. Popular striker who netted 44 goals in 105 League games in his two spells at Deepdale (6)

Down

1. Nickname given to the North End side that dominated the early history of the Football League (11)

3 and 10 down Much travelled striker who joined North End from Middlesbrough in the summer of 1971 (4,9)

4. Member of Manchester United's European Cup winning team of 1968 who arrived at Deepdale in November 1973 (6)

5. Scot ..... who managed North End from 1953 to 1954 (5)

7. North End's current longest serving player (10)

10. See 3 down

12. Ex-Blades defender who played in 200 League games (6)

15. He scored three goals in the first four games of 1983-84 (5)

Crossword (8) answers on page 150

Across

1. North End's keenest rivals (9)

6. Shortened Bolton manager! (3)

7. Malta-born forward who later played for Lancashire rivals Bolton Wanderers and Bury (7)

8. Number worn by Alex Dawson (4)

9. Scottish international and one of the finest forwards of all-time (5)

11. Italian League club that offered Tom Finney a signing on fee of £10,000 (7)

14. Managed North End to the Second Division championship in 1950-51 (5)

15. and 10 down Team that put North End out of last season's Football League Cup (9,7)

16. and 13 down See 13 down

Down

1. One time theological student, he was one of the fastest strikers ever to wear North End's colours (5)

2. North End's opponents in the Football League War Cup Final (7)

3. Former Manchester United apprentice eager to play for North End (4)

4. Number worn by Roy Tunks (3)

5. One of the finest outside-rights in the country, and an England international, he left Deepdale to play for Bradford City (4)

9. Much travelled striker who made his North End debut as a 16-year-old substitute (6)

10. See 15 across

11. Tom .....,who played for North End in the late 1890s (5)

12. Seasonal player signed from Crewe Alexandra (6)

13. and 16 across Experienced Aston Villa winger signed for £1,750 in 1935 (3,9)

Manchester United Connection

1. Two former North End favourites went on to manage Manchester United in the 1970s. Who were they?

2. Michael Appleton made one senior appearance for Manchester United in the Coca Cola Cup. Against which team?

3. Three former Manchester United players managed North End in the 1970s and 80s - who were they?

4. Which player did North End sign from Manchester United in November 1973?

5. Which current United star had a loan spell at North End in 1996?

6. Alex Ferguson's current No 2 is a former North End manager - who is he?

7. Name the former Manchester United player signed by Bobby Charlton from Southampton in 1973?

8. Played for Manchester United as an amateur whilst still at university. Joined North End at the end of his career - who is he?

9. Why did North End meet Man United at Deepdale in April 1978?

10. Who was the popular centre forward signed from Manchester United in October 1961?

11. North End signed three players from Manchester United this summer, Michael Appleton was one, who were the other two?

12. Nobby Stiles joined North End from United - how many appearances did he make for the Lilywhites? Was it 46, 106 or 146?

13. In which season did North End last play Manchester United in a league game?

14. When was the last time North End beat Manchester United in a first team game?

15. Michael Appleton was North End's record signing when coming from Old Trafford this summer. How much was the deal worth?

16. North End played an FA Cup fifth round replay at Old Trafford in 1962, against which team?

17. Who was United's leading goal scorer before North End signed him in 1937? He went on to score the winner in the 1938 FA Cup final.

18. Bobby Charlton originally came to Deepdale as manager, but ended up playing again. How many times did he play for the club?

19. Who played 36 times for Manchester United before joining North End in March 1963 for £11,500? Was it Nobby Stiles, Noddy Holder or Nobby Lawton?

20. When did North End last play Manchester United in an FA Cup semi final? (be careful!)

Answers on page 141

Midfielders

Our midfield generals are as good as we've had in many years. What rank can you reach in midfield? They are fairly easy questions and it shouldn't be too much of a battle.

1. For which country would Graeme Atkinson be eligible to play, other than England?

2. In which town was Lee Ashcroft born?

3. From which club did North End sign Graeme Atkinson?

4. Name Julian Darby's three previous clubs.

5. Which club did Simon Davey begin his career with?

6. Who was voted last year's Young Player of the Year?

7. How much did North End pay Wolves for Mark Rankine?

8. Against which club did Mark Rankine score his first league goal for North End?

9. Which Second Division club did Michael Appleton go on loan to last season?

10. Which team did Paul McKenna make his first team debut against?

11. In what year was Julian Darby born - 1968, 1967 or 1970?

12. How many full first team appearances did Graeme Atkinson make during the 1996/97 season?

13. Against which club did Michael Appleton make his North End debut?

14. Apart from North End which other clubs has Lee Ashcroft played for?

15. How much did North End pay Carlisle for Simon Davey - £50,000, £75,000 or £100,000?

16. In what month did North End sign Mark Rankine last season?

17. Against which club did Lee Ashcroft score his first league goal this season?

18. After Michael Appleton signed for North End the average age of the squad was - 19, 21 or 23?

19. Who played No.6 against Blackburn in both rounds of this year's Coca-Cola cup?

20. Which club was Sean Gregan signed from?

Answers on page 142

The Scottish Connection

At various points in North End's history the team should have wore kilts not shorts! See how much you remember of these famous Scots!

1. From which Scottish club did North End sign the legendary Alex James - Raith, Falkirk or Arbroath?

2. Which player joined North End in 1937, for £2,250, from Kilmarnock?

3. Signed from Raith Rovers in 1966 before joining Nottingham Forest in 1972. Who was he?

4. Scottish player who joined North End from Sunderland in 1967. Who was he?

5. North End had no fewer than seven Scottish internationals in their side in the late 1930s. Shankly, Mutch, O'Donnell, Dougal, Bobbie Beatie were five, name one of the other two?

6. In the 1965-66 season, a record number of Scottish-born players were on North End's books. How many? 14, 15 or 16?

7. Which former North End manager played 352 games for Rangers before the war, was it Tom Muirhead, Tommy Docherty or John McGrath?

8. Joe Dunn was signed from Clyde in 1951, for how much? £1,500, £15,000 or £150,000?

9. David Moyes played for three different Scottish clubs, name them.

10. Which Scottish club did Kelham O'Hanlon play for?

11. Which Scottish team beat North End in the quarter finals of the Anglo-Scottish Cup in 1979/80, was it Celtic, Morton or Hibernian?

12. Which Scottish team did Scottish Youth International Alex Spark join when leaving North End in the 1970s, was it Motherwell, Airdrie or Ayr?

13. How many times did Tom Finney play for England against the 'Auld Enemy'? was it 4, 7 or 12?

14. How many players have won caps for Scotland whilst at North End - is it 6, 9 or 15?

15. North End sold Ray Sharpe to which Scottish club?

16. North End signed Hugh O'Donnel from Celtic in 1935. In what year did he leave, was it 1937, 38 or 39?

17. Which Scottish born player held the record number of league appearances for North End before it was broken by Alan Kelly in 1974?

18. Which Scottish international did North End sell to Burnley, even though he had scored 39 goals in 69 games for the club?

19. Who joined North End from Scottish team Hilton Athletic in 1958 and played until 1972?

20. Which Scottish born manager was succeeded by Alan Ball Snr in 1970?

Answers on page 142

Current Premiership Managers

In this quiz, we will tell you the name of the team, all you have to do is name their manager. This is a risky quiz because football being what it is, probably half of those managers you manage to name will be sacked or will have resigned before the end of the season!

1. Liverpool

2. Everton

3. Manchester United

4. Arsenal

5. Blackburn Rovers

6. Leicester City

7. Chelsea

8. Derby County

9. Newcastle United

10. Leeds United

11. Aston Villa

12. West Ham

13. Coventry City

14. Crystal Palace

15. Tottenham

16. Wimbledon

17. Sheffield Wednesday

18. Bolton

19. Barnsley

20. Southampton

(answers as of October 1 1997)

Answers on page 142

The Plastic Pitch

Long since confined to the football dustbin - the plastic pitch has long since gone and good riddance. What can you recall about it!

1. Who was the leading league marksman on the 'plastic'?

2. Against which team did North End play their last game on the 'plastic'?

3. North End's best league win on the 'plastic' was 6-0 - against which team?

4. Which team were North End's last League opponents on the 'plastic'? Was it Carlisle, Coventry or Chesterfield?

5. In which season was the 'plastic' first used?

6. North End played 182 league games on the 'plastic' - how many did they win?

7. North End had a gate of 17,592 v Burnley on the 'plastic' in April 88. In which competition?

8. Who scored a hat-trick on his Deepdale debut, on the 'plastic'?

9. Which defunct league club were unbeaten in three league games on the 'plastic'?

10. Two teams played 7 league games on the 'plastic'. One was Wigan which was the other?

11. Only 3 of the team that played in the last game on the 'plastic' remain at North End. Who are they?

12. Two North End players scored three hat-tricks on the 'plastic' - Tony Ellis was one, who was the other?

13. Who scored North End's last ever goal on the 'plastic'?

14. North End were not the only league side with a plastic pitch. Name the other three?

15. Which current Premiership side beat North End 4-1 on the 'plastic' in October 89?

16. Which was North End's best league season on the 'plastic'?

17. Who played in goal in North End's last game on the 'plastic'?

18. Which top class referee was in charge of the last ever game on the 'plastic'?

19. North End played a non-league side in front of 16,000 plus on the 'plastic' in 1986 - which team?

20. Who did North End play in the first ever league game on the 'plastic'?

Answers on page 143

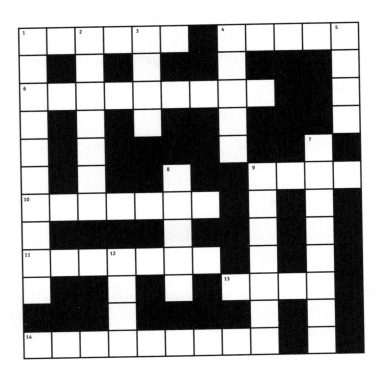

Crossword (9) answers on page 151

Across

1. The club's highest League goalscorer in any one season (6)

4. One of the club's most consistent scorers, he netted 157 goals in 363 League appearances in two spells (5)

6. and 9 across Signed from Blackburn Rovers, he later played for Bury and Bolton Wanderers (9)

9. See 6 across

10. Alec Ashworth's first club (7)

11. North End comedian of the early 1970s ? (7)

13. Ryan or Brian .....(4)

14. Member of Preston's FA Cup Final sides of 1937 and 1938, he later emigrated to Canada (9)

Down

1. Indian-born midfielder (10)

2. England amateur international full-back who joined the club from Port Vale (7)

3. Andy Fensome was the club's only .....- present in 1994-95 (4)

4. Former Manchester City centre-half who later became North End's manager (5)

5. England 'B' international goalkeeper (4)

7. Former Derby County winger he joined North End from Tulsa Roughnecks (8)

8. Former Bolton midfielder who gave North End six years loyal service (5)

9. Huge goalkeeper with a great reputation (7)

12. North End manager 1970-1973 (4)

North End beat the Seasiders in the F.A Cup in November 1994. Fill in the team sheet for the game and the scorer and three subs.

Answers on page 152

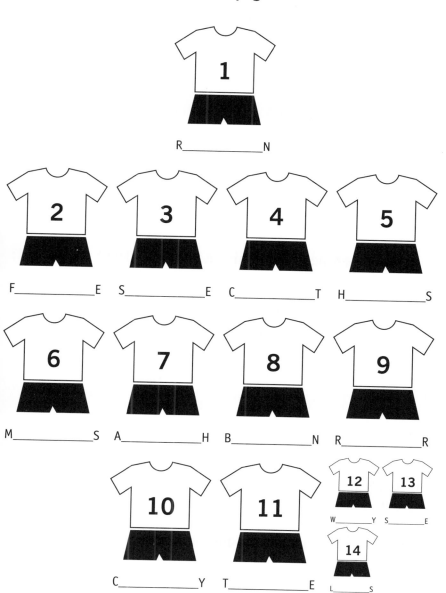

R_____N

F_____E   S_____E   C_____T   H_____S

M_____S   A_____H   B_____N   R_____R

C_____Y   T_____E

W_____Y   S_____E

L___S

Tom Finney (2)

Another Tom Finney quiz! Well he is the greatest North End player ever and a mere 20 questions could not do justice to the great man.

1. Which other league club did Tom Finney play for?

2. How many domestic honours did he win at North End?

3. In what year was Tom registered as a professional?

4. In what year did he make his football league debut?

5. In what year did he make his international debut for England?

6. How many times was Tom top scorer for North End?

7. Is Tom left handed or right handed?

8. How many times was Tom on the losing side for England; 4, 12 or 9?

9. Against which international side did he score a hat trick in England's 5-3 victory in 1950?

10. How many different postions did he play in for North End, was it 2, 3 or 5?

11. How many different positions did he play in for England, was it 2, 3 or 5?

12. How many bookings did Tom receive during his career?

13. In 1957 Finney played for England V Scotland. Which North End team mate won his only England cap in the same game?

14. In what year did Tom Finney retire?

15. What age was he when he hung up his boots?

16. Finney played in the 1950 World Cup side that surprisingly lost to which team?

17. What happened to North End the year after Finney retired?

18. Against which club did Tom make his football league debut - Wimbledon, Accrington Stanley or Leeds United?

19. Which Irish team did Finney play in the European Cup for?

20. Which title does Tom Finney now hold at North End?

Answers on page 143

The Blackburn Connection

1. North End have so far only drawn Blackburn once in the FA Cup - in which year? 1926, 1936 or 1956?

2. Prior to 1997, North End have only once drawn Blackburn in the League Cup - was it in 1974, 1975 or 1976?

3. Which current North End player also played for Blackburn Rovers?

4. Which member of the North End coaching staff played for Blackburn Rovers for eight seasons from 1979?

5. In March 1979, North End completed a league double over Rovers, a result which effectively relegated them. Who scored North End's winner?

6. Who scored North End's goal in the second leg of this year's Co Cola Cup clash?

7. When North End beat Blackburn in the League Cup in the 1970s, Ray Treacy scored one of the goals, which player, who went on to win a European Cup Winners medal with Aston Villa, scored the other goal to win 2-0?

8. Which recent North End keeper also played for Rovers in the 1980s?

9. In March 1881, Rovers beat North End by a massive scoreline, was it 10-0, 12-0 or 16-0?

10. North End's first league meeting with Blackburn away, was not played at Ewood Park, where was it played?

11. Which North End manager joined North End from Blackburn Rovers in 1949, having previously been player, coach and club secretary for North End until 1947?

12. In what season did North End last play Rovers in a league game?

13. Is Ewood Park nearer to Deepdale than Bloomfield Road?

14. Which player did North End sign from Blackburn in 1949 for £16,000, was it Bobby Langton, Harry Lowe or Gordon Lee?

15. In 1959, North End played an FA Cup fifth round replay at Ewood Park, against which Lancashire team?

16. Which non-league side did North End play at Ewood Park in the FA Cup round 2 in 1986?

17. Which North End keeper signed for Blackburn in 1961 and ended his career at Barrow?

18. Which former North End trainee scored a hat trick in a recent reserve match between the two sides?

19. Blackburn bought North End striker Eddie Quigley in 1951/52 for how much? £23,500, £53,500 or £73,500?

20. When did North End last beat Rovers?

Answers on page 143

Names

A nice easy one for you - just give us the first name of the following recent North End players.

1. G. Nebbeling

2. A. Fensome

3. G. Lancashire

4. M. Conroy

5. J. Vaughan

6. G. Bennett

7. G. Ainsworth

8. R. Sharpe

9. S. Wilkinson

10. A. Kelly

11. M. Flynn

12. T. Ellis

13. K. Magee

14. C. Sully

15. P. Raynor

16. I. Bryson

17. B. Richardson

18. M. Brown

19. A. Saville

20. B. Mimms

Answers on page 144

Firsts and Lasts

Many great players have made their debut for North End and many have ended their careers at Deepdale. North End's history is full of firsts and lasts - first to win the double, first to win the league and so on. See what you know of the club's history.

1. Which team did North End play in their first ever game in the old Fourth Division?

2. The first and only time North End have had to apply for a 're-election' was in which year?

3. Which footballer scored the last First Division goal seen at Deepdale back in 1961?

4. Against which team was Tom Finney's first ever full England game?

5. Who scored North End's first penalty goal?

6. Against which teams did Tom Finney make his first and last league appearances?

7. Who was North End's first ever manager?

8. Which company were North End's first ever shirt sponsors?

9. Which team did North End play in their last ever league game at Deepdale in the old First Division?

10. Which team did North End play in their first ever League

Cup tie?

11. Nigel Jemson made his first appearance for North End in a 4-0 defeat at Aldershot. How old was he?

12. Alan Kelly Jnr made his first appearance for North End in the same season as Nigel Jemson, which one?

13. Peter Thompson made his first appearance for North End v Arsenal in 1960/61. How old was he? 17, 18 or 19?

14. Which team did North End play in their first ever FA Cup Final in 1888?

15. Which team did North End play in their first Wembley Cup Final?

16. Which team did North End play in their last Wembley appearance?

17. George Mutch scored the first ever FA Cup Final penalty - but which team did North End sign him from?

18. North End were founder members of the Football League. Who were their first ever league opponents?

19. The first and only player to appear at Wembley as a North End player, trainer and manager - who was he?

20. Which team did North End play when Jonathan Macken made his first team debut?

Answers on page 144

Pre-1945

If your old enough to remember these then you're definitely on a pension - but for most this is a tough quiz.

1. In 1938, North End lost the Charity Shield to which team?

2. Who was the popular keeper signed from Burton Town in March 1937?

3. Who was the football legend signed from Carlisle in 1932-33?

4. Which side beat North End in the 1937 FA Cup final?

5. North End reached the final again in 1938 beating Huddersfield. What was the score? 1-0, 2-1 or 2-0?

6. North End lost the 1922 FA Cup final to Huddersfield. Where was the game played?

7. Ted Harper scored a record 37 goals for North End - in which season? 1932/33, 33/34 or 34/35?

8. North End won Division Two twice before the war, once in 1903/04. Which season did they win it a second time?

9. In what year was the now closed Spion Kop built?

10. How many League games did Tom Finney play before the war? 0, 10 or 20?

11. Father of Gordon Milne, this popular player was a permanent fixture in the 1930s for North End, who was he?

12. Who was the first player to take and score from the penalty spot in a Wembley FA Cup Final?

13. Bob Kelly was the oldest player to turn out for North End v Everton in January 1935. How old was he? 37, 40, 43?

14. North End's record league victory is 10-0. Which team did they beat?

15. What was the nickname given to North End's first 'great side'?

16. North End won the double in 1888/89. How many games did they lose?

17. During the war, North End played several matches at who's ground in Leyland?

18. Bill Tremelling was a regular member of the team in the 1930s, but which local rivals did he later coach? Burnley, Blackpool or Bury?

19. Alec Reid was signed from which Scottish club for £2,250? Was it Celtic, Aberdeen or Hibernian?

20. Bill Shankly won a single cap for Scotland in 1938 - was it against Italy, England or Northern Ireland?

Answers on page 145

So you think you're a NorthEnder

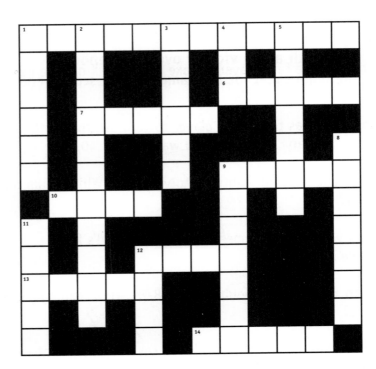

Crossword (10) answers on page 151

Across

1. and 10 across North End's opponents in the FA Cup Final of 1938 (12,4)

6. Scored all three goals in a 3-2 win over Blackpool in 1992-93 (5)

7. North End's top scorer in 1948-49 with 12 goals in 24 games (5)

9. Scorer of the goal that beat 1 across in the Final (5)

10. See 1 across

12. Former Stoke forward who returned to the Victoria Ground after scoring 42 goals in 144 first team games (4)

13. 5 down scored in both games against this club in 1980-81 (5)

14. Former Manchester United apprentice who played in 110 League games for North End (5)

Down

1. Mel or Doug? (6)

2. Beaten 7-4 in December 1947 (5,6)

3. Tough-tackling defender who played in 336 League games for North End at the turn of the century (6)

4. Central defender who had two loan spells at Deepdale in the 1990-91 season (3)

5. Signed from Nottingham Forest for a then club record fee of 95,000 (7)

8. He both played for and managed North End (7)

9. Known as 'Bud' (7)

11. Irish and England international North Enders (5)

12. Cold-sounding forward who made just one appearance in 1989-90 (4)

North End won the 1996 Third Division Championship with a 2-0 victory over Hartlepool.
Fill in the team sheet for the game and the scorers and subs.

Answers on page 152

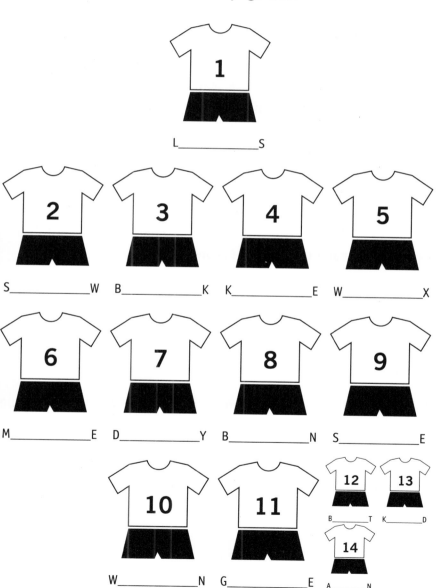

Past Strikers

Another Toughie!

1. Charlie Wayman was top scorer in Division One in season 1952/53. How many goals did he score for North End? 24, 30 or 36?

2. Who was the talented young striker signed by Brian Clough at Nottingham Forest for £150,000 in 1987?

3. Which popular North End striker was known as 'The Black Prince'?

4. Jimmy Ross holds the club individual goalscoring record in a game - how many goals did he score?

5. Which player holds the record for being the club's top scorer in the most number of seasons?

6. Which player scored a hat trick inside 11 minutes when North End beat West Ham 3-0 in the 1937 FA Cup run?

7. Which prolific goalscorer found the net 56 times in 166 league appearances for North End before joining Newcastle?

8. North End's all time greatest league goal scorer is Tom Finney. Two players share second spot. Who?

9. Which team did North End beat 8-0 in February 1958?

10. Which striker did North End sign from Aston Villa for £37,000 in June 1955?

11. Which former North End striker made a name for himself when signed by Bill Shankly, going on to win two League Championship medals and an FA Cup Winners medal?

12. Although he was leading striker in his first season, North End still needed to apply for re-election for the only time. Who was he?

13. This striker scored 54 goals in just 115 league games for North End and made his debut in September 1953. Who was he?

14. Which player scored a 4 minute hat trick for North End in the 9-0 win over Cardiff City in May 1966?

15. Which team did Steve Elliott join after leaving Deepdale?

16. Which London club bought Mike Elwiss in 1978? Was it Crystal Palace, Fulham or Wimbledon?

17. Only one of North End's top ten best ever league goal scorers is still playing - who is it?

18. Only six players have hit 100 or have made league goals for North End. Apart from Tom Finney and Alex Bruce, name the others.

19. Eddie Quigley became the most expensive player in the UK when joining North End in 1949 for £26,000, but which team did he go to after Deepdale?

20. Who is the former North End striker now more famous in Spain as a football commentator?

Answers on page 145

World Cup Quiz

In this quiz, we test your knowledge of previous World Cup tournaments. So, get your thinking caps on.

1. In what year was the World Cup first played?

2. Who were the first winners?

3. Who won the World Cup in 1934?

4. Who did they beat in the final?

5. By what score did Italy beat Hungary in the 1938 final?

6. In which country was the 1950 tournament held?

7. Who won the World Cup in 1954?

8. How many times have the Germans won the World Cup?

9. In which European city was the 1958 final held?

10. Who won the World Cup in 1962?

11. What was the score after ninety minutes in the 1966 final?

12. Who knocked England out of the 1970 World Cup?

13. By what score did Brazil beat Italy in the 1970 World Cup?

14. West Germany beat Holland 2-1 in the 1974 World Cup final, but which side scored first?

15. Who managed England when they won the World Cup?

16. In which South American city was the 1978 final held?

17. In which country were the 1982 finals held?

18. By what score did Argentina beat West Germany in the 1986 World Cup final?

19. Which team did Argentina beat in the 1990 World Cup semi finals?

20. Who did Brazil beat in the 1994 World Cup final?

Answers on page 145

Preston North End Off the Pitch

In this quiz we shall simply list the job title/position of members, officials and the press connected with Preston North End FC. All you have to do is to fill in the name of the person who holds that position. Does that sound difficult? Well, it shouldn't do to any PNE fan who knows their stuff. Here we go then.

1. President

2. Chairman

3. Deputy Chairman

4. Chief Executive

5. Finance Director

6. Preston Citizen PNE reporter

7. Team Manager

8. Head Groundsman

9. Youth Development Officer

10. Youth Coach

11. Chief Scout

12. Assistant Manager

13. Physiotherapist

14. Lancashire Evening Post Sports Editor

15. Commercial Manager

16. First Team Coach

17. Kit Manager

18. Radio Lancashire's Sports Editor

19. Red Rose 999', Sports Editor

20. Former PNE star and Match of the Day commentator

Answers on page 146

The Fans

Here are some questions concerning North End's various supporters groups. If you are not yet familiar with the work they do, or the services they offer, then this quiz is a must. Try it anyway and see how you get on.

1. North End have how many recognised supporters clubs?

2. The Preston North End's Official Supporters Club (PNEOSC) was set up in which year?

3. What was its original name? Clue: Its initials were PSRDSC.

4. The PNEOSC once held a sponsored walk across which bay?

5. They also went for a walk to which Lancashire town?

6. The PNEOSC fought against the implementation of what, in the 1980's?

7. How much does it cost adults to join the above club? Is it £400, £40 or £4 per year?

8. Joining the club entitles members to vote for whom?

9. The PNEOSC can be found at home games on which road?

10. The Southern Supporters Club has been in existence for how many years? Is it 20, 5 or 2 years?

11. And is based in which Hertfordshire town?

12. The Southern Supporters Club produces its own magazine, what's it called? (Three words)

13. What is North End's regular Fanzine called?

14. The PNEOSC is a member of the NFFSC. What do the initials stand for?

15. The PNEOSC hopes to work closely with the newly formed what? A clue - its initials are FTU.

16. The Southern Supporters Club held a special meeting last season. Who was their special guest on the night? Was it Rod Steiger, Bryan Gray or Norman Wisdom?

17. The club recently held its first ever Question Time session in association with which newspaper?

18. What is the Club's call-line number?

19. What is North End's children's supporters club called?

20. Which player is it's current president?

Answers on page 146

The Deadly Duo

In this quiz, we will be asking questions about two of North End's most prolific goalscorers of the 1970s and 1980s, Mike Elwiss and Alex Bruce. So, stand by any of you who confess to being over 35; this particular set of questions are probably right up your street.

1. Mike Elwiss spent how many seasons playing alongside Alex Bruce?

2. From which Yorkshire club did Elwiss arrive?

3. He scored two goals on his debut against which club?

4. On the final day of the 1973-74 season, North End were relegated but Elwiss managed to get on the scoresheet. How many goals did he score that day?

5. And who were North End playing that day?

6. In what year did Elwiss leave Deepdale?

7. Which club did he move to?

8. How many league games in total (all clubs) did Mike Elwiss play. Was it 314, 296, or 412?

9. How many goals in total did he score, was it 79, 100, or 152?

10. He was forced to retire prematurely from the game. Can you pinpoint what injury caused his retirement?

11. In which Scottish city was Alex Bruce born?

12. In what year did young Bruce join North End?

13. He made his debut three seasons later against which club?

14. Which club was he transferred to originally?

15. Alex returned to Deepdale in what year?

16. And which player left the club as part of the same deal?

17. The above move caused which North End player/manager to resign?

18. Which Lancashire club did Bruce eventually leave North End for?

19. How many games did Alex Bruce play in his full career. Was it 277, 394, or 411?

20. In his full career, how many goals did he manage to score, was it 210, 194 or 167?

Answers on page 146

North End's first ever game in Division Three against Halifax.
Fill in the team sheet for the game and the scorers

Answers on page 152

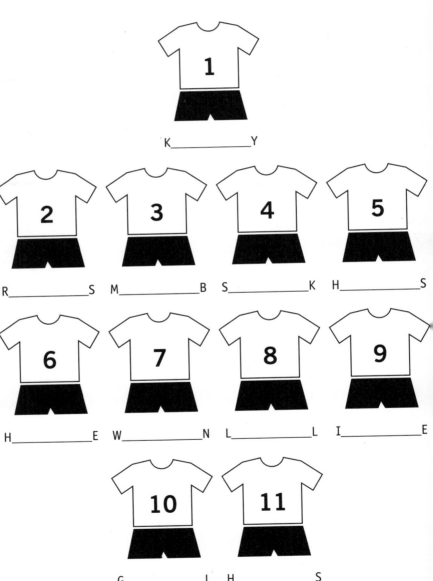

K_____Y

R_____S M_____B S_____K H_____S

H_____E W_____N L_____L I_____E

G_____L H_____S

Who are we?

Answers on page 152

Can you name this popular former keeper?

Name the two North End favourites in this shot?

Answers.

Championship Year 1995-1996

1. Lincoln City
2. Plymouth Argyle
3. Wigan Athletic
4. 0-0
5. Cambridge United
6. Andy Saville
7. 2-2
8. Fulham
9. 4-0
10. 6-0
11. David Moyes
12. Four points
13. Gillingham
14. Cardiff City
15. 5-0
16. Four Points
17. Rochdale
18. Andy Saville
19. 2-0
20. Exeter City

Current Squad

1. Manchester United
2. West Bromwich Albion
3. Hull City
4. Cambridge United
5. West Bromwich Albion
6. Carlisle United
7. Darlington
8. Blackburn Rovers
9. Bury
10. Port Vale
11. Manchester United
12. Jaro
13. Manchester United
14. Burnley
15. Burnley
16. Wolves
17. Carlisle United
18. Crystal Palace
19. PNE Youth Policy
20. PNE Youth Policy

Promotion

1. 9
2. 1903-04
3. Second Division
4. Blackpool
5. 1-0
6. Burnley
7. 9
8. 15
9. 1950-51
10. 20
11. Tom Finney, Charlie Wayman, Angus Morrison
12. Craven Cottage
13. Ricky Heppolette

14. Rotherham United
15. 1977-78. Champions Wrexham drew their last game 0-0 against Peterborough United, allowing third placed Preston to go up on goal difference.
16. John McGrath
17. Orient
18. Les Chapman
19. John Thomas
20. Hartlepool

Deepdale
1. 1875
2. Preston Nelson
3. Moor Park
4. Women
5. 1921
6. £19,000
7. 1934
8. 1936
9. Arsenal
10. 42,684
11. £250
12. 1953
13. Bolton Wanderers
14. £500,000
15. Steel
16. 1995
17. March
18. Walsall
19. Prince Charles
20. 8,000

Highs and Lows
1. 1927-28
2. Tommy Thompson (34); Tom Finney (26)
3. Aston Villa
4. Ted Harper
5. Archie Gemmill
6. Chelsea
7. 23rd in October
8. One
9. Alex Bruce - 8 times in 10 seasons
10. Sheffield Wednesday
11. Stoke
12. Blackpool
13. 1985
14. Scunthorpe United when just 2,007 fans turned up
15. Floodlight difficulties
16. Northampton Town
17. Cardiff City
18. Nine
19. 10,018
20. Alex Dawson

The League Cup
1. Norwich
2. WBA
3. McIlmoyle
4. Tranmere, Chester, Scarborough, Sunderland, Burnley, Stoke, Stockport
5. 18
6. Aston Villa
7. Barrow
8. Michael Holt

9. Gary Brazil
10. 0 - the competition started a year after he retired
11. 4-1
12. Port Vale
13. Ron Atkinson
14. 1986/87
15. Bobby Mimms as part of a transfer deal.
16. Warren Joyce
17. Ray Treacy
18. Bryson, Cartwright
19. Alex Bruce
20. QPR

The League Cup 1970's

1. Tottenham Hotspur
2. Watford
3. Workington Town
4. Bolton Wanderers
5. Chester City
6. Two legged ties
7. Blackburn Rovers
8. Hull City
9. 4-2
10. Bury
11. Port Vale
12. Walsall
13. Second
14. 5-2
15. QPR
16. 3-1
17. 3-1
18. Fourth round
19. Tottenham Hotspur
20. Potts

The League Cup 1980's

1. West Brom Albion
2. Wigan
3. 0-0
4. Two legged second round ties
5. Leicester City
6. 4-1
7. 4-2
8. Steve Elliott
9. Tranmere Rovers
10. 2-2
11. Norwich City
12. 9-4
13. Blackpool
14. 5-2
15. 0-0
16. 2-1 to the P.N.E
17. West Ham
18. West Brom Albion
19. Shaw
20. Four times in total

The League Cup 1990's

1. Chester City
2. 5-3
3. Scarborough
4. 7-6
5. Joyce
6. Stoke City
7. 5-2
8. Burnley
9. Ellis
10. Cartwright
11. Stockport County
12. Fensome (Pen)

13. Moyes
14. Sunderland
15. 1-1
16. 2-3
17. Cartwright
18. Sunderland
19. 5-1
20. None

Goalkeepers (1)

1. Arthur Wharton
2. Ghana
3. James Trainer
4. Wales
5. Dr R.H. Mills-Roberts
6. 6
7. Fred Mitchell
8. Huddersfield Town
9. Everton
10. One
11. Jack Fairbrother
12. Dublin
13. 447
14. 1973
15. Bobby Mimms
16. David Lucas
17. West Germany
18. 1974
19. Bobby Mimms
20. Kelham O'Hanlon

Tommy Docherty

1. Glasgow
2. Celtic
3. 1949
4. £4,000

5. Leeds United
6. Outside left
7. Right half
8. The Doc
9. Wales
10. 1952
11. Arsenal
12. £28,000
13. Cliff Britton
14. Chelsea
15. 1981
16. 1977
17. 1971
18. Bill Shankly
19. Chelsea, Rotherham United, QPR, Aston Villa, Porto, Manchester United, Preston
20. Admitting to an affair with a married woman

Managers

1. Tommy Docherty, Nobby Stiles, Gordon Lee
2. A committee
3. Bobby Charlton, Nobby Stiles, Brian Kidd
4. Jimmy Milne sold son Gordon Milne
5. Cambridge Utd.
6. Portsmouth
7. Tommy Booth
8. John Bird to Newcastle
9. Will Scott
10. Brian Kidd
11. Harry Catterick
12. Vincent Hayes

13. 19
14. None
15. Frank O'Farrell
16. Les Chapman
17. Tommy Docherty
18. Jimmy Milne
19. Cliff Britton
20. David Moyes

Tom Finney (1)
1. The Preston Plumber
2. Leeds United
3. 76
4. 1957
5. 26
6. Portugal
7. 30
8. 38
9. WBA
10. 187
11. Bill Shankly
12. 1950/51
13. 1996/97
14. N Ireland, USSR
15. 1922
16. Luton
17. 443
18. 23
19. 21
20. none

Backroom Staff
1. Birmingham City, Blackburn Rovers, Preston North End
2. Alan Fogarty
3. Chris Sulley

4. Halifax Town
5. 13
6. Bolton Wanderers
7. April
8. Blackpool
9. Vancouver Whitecaps
10. David Moyes
11. 1975
12. Peter McCallion
13. 1996
14. Auto Windscreen Shield Trophy
15. Coventry, Middlesborough, Wimbledon
16. Peter Church
17. December 1994
18. Charlton Athletic
19. Newcastle United
20. Kevin Tamati

Present Strikers
1. Rossendale
2. Blackburn Rovers
3. Rotherham Utd.
4. 27
5. £150,000
6. Stockport County
7. 15
8. Kurt Nogan
9. Wales
10. Ole Solskjaer
11. Blackburn Rovers
12. Burnley
13. 1992
14. Rotherham Utd.
15. Birkenhead

16. Sheffield
17. 4
18. Braveheart
19. Tennis
20. Gambling

FA Cup Finals
1. **Year** 1888
Opponents West Bromwich Albion **Score** 1-2
2. **Year** 1889
Opponents Wolverhampton Wanderers **Score** 3-0
3. **Year** 1922
Opponents Huddersfield Town **Score** 0-1
4. **Year** 1937
Opponents Sunderland **Score** 1-3
5. **Year** 1938
Opponents Huddersfield Town **Score** 1-0aet
6. **Year** 1954
Opponents West Bromwich Albion **Score** 2-3
7. **Year** 1964
Opponents West Ham United **Score** 2-3
1. 1883
2. Great Lever
3. 26-0
4. Hyde
5. Fred Dewhurst
6. Frank O'Donnell
7. Angus Morrison
8. Doug Holden

9. Second Division
10. Ian Davidson

FA Cup 1970's
1. Manchester United
2. Bristol City
3. Grimsby Town
4. Fulham
5. Carlisle United
6. 3-2
7. Crewe
8. Anfield
9. Halifax Town
10. Second
11. Derby County
12. Blyth Spartans
13. Bishop Auckland
14. Bobby Charlton
15. Bruce
16. Manchester United
17. Lincoln City
18. Elwiss and Bruce
19. Eleven
20. Fourth

FA Cup 1980's
1. Ipswich Town
2. 4-3
3. Doyle
4. Shepshed Charterhouse
5. Blackpool
6. Leeds United
7. First
8. Telford United
9. Bury
10. Walsall

11. 7-3
12. Blackburn (Ewood Park)
13. 5-0
14. Middlesborough
15. 2-0
16. First
17. Tranmere Rovers
18. 3-0
19. Ipswich Town
20. Once

FA Cup 1990's

1. Tranmere Rovers
2. Joyce
3. Whitley Bay
4. 1-0
5. Fog
6. 1-1
7. Thomas
8. Sheffield Wednesday
9. 5-4
10. David Moyes
11. Kidderminster
12. 1-0
13. 1-0 to the PNE
14. 14,036
15. Walsall
16. Two
17. Bradford City
18. Sheffield Wednesday
19. Fourth Round (1993-94)
20. York City

FA Cup Semi Finals

1. (a) West Bromwich
(b) Trent Bridge
2. (a) Crewe Alexandra
(b) Anfield
3. (a) West Bromwich
(b) Bramall Lane
4. (a) Everton
(b) Bramall Lane
5. (a) Everton
(b) Bramall Lane
6. (a) Everton
(b) Ewood Park
7. (a) Tottenham
(b) Hillsborough
8. (a) Tottenham
(b) Hillsborough
9. (a) West Bromwich
(b) Highbury
10. (a) Aston Villa
(b) Bramall Lane
11. (a) Sheffield Wednesday
(b) Maine Road
12. (a) Swansea Town (as they were) (b) Villa Park

Penalties

1. Jack Gordon
2. Blackburn Rovers
3. 1904
4. Derby County
5. John Pears
6. Joe Beresford
7. The North End players were adamant that the foul on Billy Smith took place outside the area
8. Mitchell
9. Aberdeen

10. 120 minutes
11. Huddersfield Town
12. West Bromwich Albion
13. Thompson
14. Tommy Docherty
15. Goalkeepers can now move along their goal line when facing a penalty kick, but must have both feet on the line and not move forward at any time
16. The ball hit PNE's keeper on the right arm before being deflected into the net
17. 1891
18. 0-0
19. Hesford
20. Ian Bryson

Bill Shankly
1. £500
2. 1938
3. 25
4. 1
5. 1932/33
6. Herbal tea
7. Carlisle United
8. 1959
9. 5ft 7ins
10. 1981
11. 1949
12. Five
13. 1965
14. Huddersfield Town
15. 296
16. First
17. 1974

18. Andy Beattie
19. Joe Lewis
20. Three

The 1950's
1. 1959
2. 1952/53, 1957/58
3. Burnley lost 2-3
4. 1950/51
5. Willie Forbes
6. 1952
7. 1957/58
8. Will Scott, Scott Symon, Frank Hill, Cliff Britton
9. Doug Holden (for Bolton)
10. Dennis Hatsell
11. Gordon Milne
12. Joe Marston
13. Angus Morrison
14. Frank O'Farrell
15. Palermo
16. Willie Cunningham
17. Fred Else
18. WBA
19. Sheffield Wednesday 2-0 at Maine Road
20. South Africa

Transfers
1. Caledonian Thistle for £15,000
2. £55,000
3. Michael Appleton
4. Eddie Quigley
5. Michael Robinson, June 1979 for £765,000

6. Bradford City
7. Ricky Heppolette
8. Francis Burns & Nobby Stiles
9. WBA
10. Wrexham
11. Mansfield Town
12. Alan Kelly
13. Gareth Ainsworth
14. Free transfer
15. Brighton
16. Tony Ellis
17. Mike Flynn
18. Paul Raynor
19. Julian Darby
20. Shrewsbury Town

Football Anagrams

1. George Best
2. Alan Shearer
3. David Seaman
4. Pele
5. Glen Hoodle
6. Jimmy Greaves
7. Les Ferdinand
8. Kenny Dalglish
9. David Beckham
10. Bobby Moore
11. Gazza
12. Zola
13. Mark Lawrenson
14. Jack Charlton
15. Danny Blanchflower
16. Stanley Matthews
17. Gordon Banks
18. Gary Lineker
19. Peter Shilton

20. Trevor Brooking

Gary Peters

1. 44
2. John Beck
3. Aldershot
4. none
5. 431
6. Aldershot, Reading, Wimbledon, Fulham
7. Fulham, Reading
8. Cambridge United
9. 22
10. Three, once with Wimbledon, twice with Reading
11. Walsall (FA Cup 2nd round 1-1)
12. Hereford 4-2
13. No
14. David Moyes
15. None Preston North End was his first managerial job
16. Amazingly none, even though North End were champions
17. Once in February 1997
18. None
19. Reading
20. 5th in Division Three

Goalkeepers (2)

1. Malaysia
2. Harry Holdcroft
3. 1960-61
4. Bristol City

5. Alan (Sheff Utd)
Gary (Oldham)
6. Steve Woods
7. Lincoln City
8. 1986
9. Rotherham Utd
10. Dundee Utd
11. Tommy Docherty
12. 380
13. Blackburn Rovers
14. Eire
15. Finland
16. The ball hit his backside and went in!
17. Crewe at Deepdale (North End lost 2-1)
18. 1973
19. Alan Kelly Snr
20. Barry Richardson

General Football
1. Manchester United
2. Wrexham
3. France
4. George Graham
5. Jurninho
6. Inter Milan
7. Three
8. Mike Channon
9. Francis Lee
10. Four
11. Chester
12. Chelsea
13. John Aldridge
14. Alf Ramsey
15. West Brom

16. Benfica
17. Lisbon
18. Italy
19. Liverpool
20. Sweden

Honours
1. The competition had ceased
2. Spurs, Arsenal, Liverpool, Manchester United
3. Swansea Town (as they were)
4. Once in 1938
5. 1957/58
6. Five 1888, 1922, 1937, 1954, 1964
7. Arsenal on goal difference
8. 1941
9. West Ham
10. Wycombe Wanderers
11. Bury
12. Michael Jackson & Gary Parkinson
13. Wolves
14. Kennington Oval
15. 61
16. 1937 North End lost 3-1 to Sunderland
17. 1960
18. 42 in 1887-88
19. 93/94 vs Bournemouth
20. September 97 round 2, leg 2, beat Blackburn 1-0

Anagrams
1. Michael Jackson
2. Kurt Nogan

3. Sean Gregan
4. Lee Ashcroft
5. David Reeves
6. Gary Parkinson
7. Colin Murdock
8. David Moyes
9. Teuvo Moilanen
10. Ryan Kidd
11. Jamie Squires
12. David Lucas
13. Michael Holt
14. Gary Peters
15. Lee Cartwright
16. Kelham O'Hanlon
17. Paul McKenna
18. Neil McDonald
19. Dean Barrick
20. Michael Appleton

Current Defenders

1. Gillingham
2. Ballymena
3. Jaro
4. Port Vale
5. Cambridge Utd
6. £125,000
7. Shrewsbury Town
8. Colchester United
9. 1994
10. Crystal Palace
11. Burnley's Player of the Season award
12. Middlesborough, Bolton, Burnley
13. Dean Barrick
14. Radcliffe
15. Darlington
16. Notts County
17. 22
18. 6ft 5ins
19. Dundee United, Carlisle, Northampton, Middlesborough, Preston
20. Dean Barrick

League Grounds

1. Bristol City
2. Southampton
3. Tranmere Rovers
4. Torquay United
5. Rochdale
6. Leyton Orient
7. Coventry City
8. Portsmouth
9. Peterborough United
10. Notts County/Swindon
11. Reading
12. Sheffield United
13. Scunthorpe United
14. Shrewsbury Town
15. West Ham
16. QPR
17. Stockport County
18. Swansea City
19. Lincoln City
20. Leicester City

1997/8 Division Two Opposition

1. AFC Bournemouth
2. Bristol Rovers at Victory Parade

3. Fulham
4. Carlisle Utd
5. Three (Millwall, Fulham and Brentford)
6. Eight (two each v Oldham, Wigan, Burnley and Blackpool)
7. Chesterfield
8. Plymouth Argyle
9. Plymouth Argyle
10. Southend
11. Watford - Graham Taylor
12. Neil Warnock
13. Michael Knighton at Carlisle
14. Walsall
15. Adams Park
16. Boothferry Cresent
17. Chesterfield
18. Blackpool
19. Robins Park in a new stadium
20. Preston of course!

Internationals
1. Tuevo Moilanen
2. 76
3. Tommy Thompson in 1957
4. Alan Kelly Snr
5. One v Poland in 1977
6. One
7. Northern Ireland
8. None, he didn't win a full cap until after leaving North End
9. Tommy Docherty - Scotland in 1971
10. Fred Dewhurst & WC Rose
11. England Ladies v West Germany Ladies, May 1997
12. Thirty
13. Isle of Man XI
14. Northern Ireland
15. 5
16. One
17. Frank O'Farrell
18. None
19. Brian Godfrey
20. Republic of Ireland

Local Rivals
1. Manchester City
2. Inter Milan
3. Liverpool
4. Roma
5. Newcastle United
6. Hearts
7. Celtic
8. Sheffield Wednesday
9. Preston
10. Chester City
11. Feyenord
12. Spurs
13. Derby County
14. Birmingham City
15. Bristol City
16. Chelsea
17. Notts County
18. Portsmouth
19. Norwich City
20. Luton Town

Manchester United Connection
1. Tommy Docherty and Frank O'Farrell

2. Crystal Palace
3. Bobby Charlton, Nobby Stiles, Brian Kidd
4. David Sadler
5. David Beckham
6. Brian Kidd
7. Francis Burns
8. Alan Gowling
9. David Sadler's testimonial
10. Alex Dawson
11. Colin Murdock and Jonathan Macken
12. 46
13. 1960-61
14. September 1959. 4-0
15. £500,000 in total subject to appearances
16. Liverpool, North End won 1-0
17. George Mutch
18. 38
19. Nobby Lawton
20. They haven't

Midfielders
1. Holland, he has a Dutch grand parent
2. Preston
3. Hull City
4. Bolton, Coventry and WBA
5. Swansea City
6. Paul McKenna
7. £80,000
8. Chesterfield
9. Grimsby Town
10. Wycombe Wanderers
11. 1967
12. 12
13. Millwall
14. West Brom & Notts County on loan
15. £75,000
16. September
17. Millwall
18. 23
19. Sean Gregan
20. Darlington

The Scottish Connection
1. Raith Rovers
2. Bobbie Beattie
3. George Lyall
4. Jim McNab
5. Andy Beattie or Tom Smith
6. 16
7. Tom Muirhead
8. £1,500
9. Celtic, Dunfermline, Hamilton
10. Dundee United
11. Morton 5-1 on aggregate
12. Motherwell
13. 7
14. 15
15. Dunfermline
16. 1939
17. Peter McBride
18. Andy McLaren
19. George Ross
20. Bobby Seith

Current Premiership Managers
1. Roy Evans

2. Howard Kendall
3. Alex Ferguson
4. Arsene Wenger
5. Roy Hodgson
6. Martin O'Neill
7. Ruud Gullit
8. Jim Smith
9. Kenny Dalglish
10. George Graham
11. Brian Little
12. Harry Redknapp
13. Gordon Strachan
14. Steve Coppull
15. Gerry Francis
16. Joe Kinnear
17. David Pleat
18. Colin Todd
19. Danny Wilson
20. Dave Jones

The Plastic Pitch

1. Tony Ellis with 45 goals
2. Torquay in the Div 3 play-offs 94
3. Chesterfield Feb 89
4. Carlisle United, April 94
5. 1986/87
6. 94
7. Sherpa Van Trophy
8. Ronnie Jepson
9. Aldershot
10. Chester City
11. Lee Cartwright, Ryan Kidd, David Moyes
12. John Thomas
13. Paul Raynor

14. Luton, Oldham and QPR
15. Bolton Wanderers
16. 1986/87 W16 D4 L3
17. Steve Woods
18. Joe Worral
19. Chorley in FA Cup
20. Swansea City

Tom Finney (2)

1. He only played for PNE
2. Only the Second Division Championship
3. 1940
4. 1946
5. 76
6. Once
7. Left
8. 1954
9. Portugal
10. 5
11. 3
12. None
13. T. Thompson
14. 1960
15. 38
16. USA
17. They were relegated
18. Leeds United
19. Distillery
20. Club President

The Blackburn Connection

1. 1926 Rovers won 4-1 after a replay
2. 1975 North End won 2-0 on aggregate

3. Michael Holt
4. Mick Rathbone
5. Alex Bruce
6. Dean Barrick
7. Tony Morley
8. Bobby Mimms
9. 16-0
10. Leamington Road
11. Will Scott
12. 1980/81 in Division 2
13. Yes
14. Bobby Langton
15. Bolton Wanderers - North End lost 0-1
16. Chorley
17. Fred Else
18. James Beattie
19. £23,500
20. In 1997 - 2nd round 2nd leg of the Coca Cola Cup

Names
1. Gavin
2. Andy
3. Graham
4. Mike
5. John
6. Gary
7. Gareth
8. Raymond
9. Steve
10. Alan
11. Mike
12. Tony
13. Kevin
14. Chris
15. Paul
16. Ian
17. Barry
18. Micky
19. Andy
20. Bobby

Firsts and Lasts
1. Peterborough
2. May 1986
3. Bobby Charlton
4. Northern Ireland September 1946
5. Jack Gordon - v Blackburn in 1891
6. First was v Leeds 1946/47; last final day on 1959/60 season was Luton Town
7. Vincent Hayes
8. Pontins
9. Manchester United at Deepdale in 1961. We lost 4-2
10. Peterborough
11. 16
12. 1985/86
13. 17
14. WBA
15. Sunderland
16. Wycombe in the 1994/95 play offs
17. Manchester United
18. Burnley - 8th September 1888, North End won 5-2
19. Jimmy Milne, player 1937, trainer 1954 and manager in 1964

20. Gillingham

Pre-1945
1. Arsenal
2. Jack Fairbrother
3. Bill Shankly
4. Sunderland
5. 1-0
6. Stamford Bridge
7. 32/33
8. 1912/13
9. 1919
10. 0
11. Jimmy Milne
12. George Mutch
13. 40
14. Stoke
15. The Invincibles
16. None
17. Leyland Motors FC
18. Blackpool
19. Aberdeen
20. England

Past Strikers
1. 24
2. Nigel Jemson
3. Alex Dawson
4. 7 goals in 26-0 win over Hyde
5. Alex Bruce, 8 out of 10 seasons
6. George Mutch
7. Gary Brazil
8. Tommy Roberts Alex Bruce with 157

9. Birmingham City
10. Tommy Thompson
11. Peter Thompson
12. John Thomas
13. Dennis Hatsell
14. Brian Godfrey
15. Luton Town
16. Crystal Palace
17. Tony Ellis (Blackpool)
18. Tommy Roberts, Tommy Thompson, Alex Dawson, Charlie Wayman
19. Blackburn Rovers
20. Michael Robinson

World Cup Quiz
1. 1930
2. Uruguay
3. Italy
4. Czechoslovakia
5. 4-2
6. Brazil
7. West Germany
8. Three
9. Stockholm
10. Brazil.
11. 2-2
12. West Germany
13. 4-1
14. Holland
15. Alf Ramsey
16. Buenos Aires
17. Spain
18. 3-2
19. Italy
20. Italy

Preson North End Off the Pitch

1. Tom Finney
2. Bryan Gray
3. Derek Shaw
4. Peter J Church
5. Tony Scholes
6. Tom Parker
7. Gary Peters
8. Peter McCallion
9. Geoff McDougle
10. Neil McDonald
11. Alan Fogarty
12. David Moyes
13. Mick Rathbone
14. Brian Ellis
15. Steve White
16. Steve Harrison
17. Brian Hickson
18. Gary Hickson
19. Nigel Reed
20. Mark Lawrenson

The Fans

1. Two
2. 1981
3. Preston and South Ribble and District Supporters Club
4. Morecambe
5. Wigan
6. I D Cards
7. £4
8. Player of the Year
9. Lowthorpe Road
10. Two
11. Watford
12. Wise Men Say
13. Pie Muncher
14. National Federation of Football Supporters Clubs
15. Football Task Unit
16. Bryan Gray
17. Lancashire Evening Post
18. 0891 660220
19. Deepdale Ducklings/Young Northenders
20. David Reeves

The Deadly Duo

1. Three
2. Doncaster Rovers
3. Carlisle United
4. Two
5. Middlesborough
6. 1978
7. Crystal Palace
8. 314
9. 79
10. Knee injury
11. Dundee
12. 1968
13. Swindon Town
14. Newcastle United
15. 1975
16. John Bird
17. Bobby Charlton
18. Wigan Athletic
19. 394
20. 167

1

¹P	L	A	²S	T	I	³C		⁴E		⁵G
O			P			H		⁶G	A	G	E
T		⁷H	O	L	M	E	S		R		M
T		N				S		L		M
⁸S	⁹U	B	S	T	I	T	U	T	E		I
	Z		O			E		S		L
¹⁰B	E	R	R	Y		R		T		L
	L		S			F		¹¹B	O	B
¹²S	A	M		¹³H		I		W		¹⁴D
	C		¹⁵C	O	L	E	M	A	N		U
			L			L				N
¹⁶F	I	R	S	T		¹⁷D	A	W	S	O	N

2

¹F	A	I	²R	B	R	O	T	H	E	R
L		A						A
O		N			⁴S		⁵L	O	W	E
O		⁶B	R	A	Z	I	L		L
D		R			M		⁷W		I
⁸L	E	Y	T	O	N	O	R	I	E	N	T
I		S			O		L		G
⁹G	O	O	C	¹⁰H			L		S
H		N		I		¹¹R	E	I	D		¹²F
T				C		A		A		O
¹³S	H	A	N	K	L	Y		M		U
			S		¹⁴O	S	H	O	R

3

¹F	²A	R	³N	⁴W	O	R	T	H		⁵L
	L		O		F					A
	L		R		A			⁶D	O	N
⁷C	A	T	T	E	R	I	C	⁸K		G
	R		H		R			E		T
	D		A		E			L		O
	Y		⁹M	E	L	H	O	L	D	¹⁰E	N
	C		P		L			Y		L
¹¹S	E	I	T	H				¹²T	W	O
H			O		¹³L	Y	O	N		I
¹⁴A	L	A	N		E				S
W			¹⁵D	E	W	H	U	R	S	T

4

¹A	S	T	²C	R	O	F	T	³T		⁴L	E	⁵S
R			O				R			A
⁶S	P	A	R	K		⁷B	E	C	T	O	N	D
E			I		⁸I		M			E
N		⁹N	O	N	L	E	A	G	U	R
A			T		G		L			S
L	¹⁰C	H	A	R	N	L	E	Y
	¹¹L		I		A		I		¹²F
	U		A		¹³M	C	N	E	I	L
	C		N			G			Y
¹⁴M	A	R	S	T	O	N		N
	S				¹⁵M	I	L	N	E

5

```
C A R D I F F C I T Y
R     A     O     H   S
A     G     R     O   I
W     G     W A Y M A N
F I V E     A     P   G
O     E     R O S S   L
R O Y   D   D     O N E
D       A L S T O N   T
        V     U       O
B O G I E     N   T E N
O         Y O R K
B E L L         S W A N N
```

6

```
P A L E T H O R P E
E     Y     D         B
T     A   A D   H Y D E
E L L I S O N       C
R     L   H U N T E R K
S         W N E
        C H O R L E Y   M
        O R L     L     O
      S M I T H   B U   O
H     M   H   L A W T O N
A     O       X   U   E
M C N A B     F I N N E Y
```

7

¹I	R	V	I	N	E		²M	³I	M	M	⁴S
N						⁵S		C		A
⁶V	I	⁷C	T	O	R	Y		⁸B	I	R	D
I		A				M		L		L
⁹N	O	R	T	¹⁰H		O		M		E
C		T		U		N	¹¹F	O	U	R
I		W		G		¹²A		Y		
¹³B	A	R	G	H		¹⁴S	T	I	L	E	¹⁵S
L		I				K		E		A
¹⁶E	I	G	H	T		¹⁷K	I	T		Y
S		H				N		¹⁸J	O	E
		¹⁹T	H	O	M	A	S			R

8

¹B	L	²A	C	³K	P	⁴O	O	L		⁵B
R		R		E		N			⁶T	O	D
O		⁷S	T	E	V	E	N	S		N
W		E		N					D
⁸N	I	N	E		⁹J	A	M	E	S
		A			E				¹⁰H
¹¹P	A	L	¹²E	R	M	O		¹³J	O
R			A		S		¹⁴S	C	O	T	T
A			S		O			E		S
¹⁵T	O	T	T	E	N	H	A	M		P
T			E						U
	¹⁶B	E	R	E	S	F	O	R	D	R

9

Across/Down grid:

Row 1: ¹H A ²R P ³E R ⬛ ⁴B R U C E ⁵E
Row 2: E ⬛ I ⬛ V ⬛ O ⬛ ⬛ ⬛ L
Row 3: ⁶P A T T E R S O N ⬛ ⬛ S
Row 4: P ⬛ C ⬛ R ⬛ T ⬛ ⬛ ⬛ E
Row 5: O ⬛ H ⬛ ⬛ ⬛ H ⬛ ⁷O ⬛
Row 6: L ⬛ I ⬛ ⁸J ⬛ ⬛ ⁹M A R K
Row 7: ¹⁰E V E R T O N ⬛ C ⬛ I ⬛
Row 8: T ⬛ ⬛ ⬛ Y ⬛ B ⬛ O ⬛
Row 9: ¹¹T A R ¹²B U C K ⬛ R ⬛ R ⬛
Row 10: E ⬛ ⬛ A ⬛ E ⬛ ¹³K I D D
Row 11: ⬛ ⬛ ⬛ L ⬛ ⬛ ⬛ D ⬛ A
Row 12: ¹⁴G A L L I M O R E ⬛ ⬛ N

10

Row 1: ¹H U ²D D E ³R S ⁴F I ⁵E L D
Row 2: O ⬛ E ⬛ O ⬛ E ⬛ L ⬛
Row 3: L ⬛ R ⬛ D ⬛ ⁶E L L I S
Row 4: D ⬛ ⁷B R O W N ⬛ I ⬛
Row 5: E ⬛ Y ⬛ A ⬛ O ⬛ ⁸C
Row 6: N ⬛ C ⬛ Y ⬛ ⁹M U T C H
Row 7: ⬛ ¹⁰T O W N ⬛ A ⬛ T ⬛ A
Row 8: ¹¹K ⬛ U ⬛ ⬛ X ⬛ P
Row 9: E ⬛ N ¹²S H A W E ⬛ M
Row 10: ¹³L U T O N ⬛ E ⬛ A
Row 11: L ⬛ Y ⬛ O ⬛ L ⬛ N
Row 12: Y ⬛ ⬛ W ¹⁴C L A R K

Team Sheet answers

Page 19
Thompson, Cunningham, Walton, Docherty, Marston, Forbes, Finney, Foster, Wayman(1), Baxter, Morrison(1).

Page 44
Kelly, Ross, Smith, Lawton, Singleton, Kendall, Wilson, Ashworth, Dawson(1), Spavin, Holden(1).

Page 57
Kelly, Ross, McNab, Bird, Hawkins, Spavin(2), Heppolette, Ham, Lloyd, Spark, Clark(1), Sub: Wilson.

Page 69
Kelly, Miller, Bennett, Atkins, Jones, Allardyce, Chapman(1), Swann, Thomas, Brazil(1), Williams. Sub: Worthington.

Page 81
Else, Wilson, Walton, Fullam, Dunn, Smith(1), Finney, Milne, Alston(1), Sneddon, Taylor.

Page 105
Richardson, Fensome, Sharpe, Cartwright, Holmes, Moyes, Ainsworth, Bryson, Raynor, Conroy(1), Trebble. Subs: Whalley, Sale, Lucas.

Page 117
Lucas, Sparrow, Barrick, Kilbane, Wilcox, Moyes, Davey(1), Bryson, Saville(1), Wilkinson, Gage. Subs: Bennett, Kidd, Atkinson.

Page 128
Kelly, Ross, McNab, Spark, Hawkins, Hepplette(1), Wilson, Lyall, Irvine, Gemmill, Hughes, Sub: Ingram.

Who Are We? answers
Page 30
Top. Frank Worthington
Bottom. Sammy McIroy

Page 45
Top. Tony Ellis
Bottom. Kevin Mooney

Page 129
Top. Alan Kelly Jnr
Bottom. Mike Elwiss & David Sadler

Spot the Programme answers

1. 1977/78 v Lincoln City, Div 3
2. 1978/79 v Leicester City, Div 2
3. 1976/77 v Walsall, Div 3
4. 1983/84 v Bradford City, Div 4
5. 1984/85 v Walsall, Div 3
6. 1974/75 v Aldershot, Div 3
7. David Sadler's Testimonial April 1978
8. 1975/76 v Port Vale, Div 3

Read on and win a season ticket

Competition

This is your chance to show how devoted a North End fan you are. We have compiled 12 extremely difficult questions. We do not expect you to answer them straight away. So much so, that we are giving you until May 31st 1998 to complete your entry. Simply send your answers to "Quiz Book Competition", Commercial House, Lowthorpe Rd, Preston, PR1 6RU. The winner will be drawn from the correct entries. The decision of Preston North End is final. The winner will receive a season ticket for 1998/99. No employees of Preston North End plc or their families may enter. No correspondence will be entered into. Do not forget to enclose you name, address, postcode and telephone number with your entry.

1. Name the goalkeeper who was capped for Wales during his time at Deepdale but never appeared in North End's first XI.

2. Which North End player won a trophy during the war for boxing in a middle-weight bout?

3. I started out with Oswestry Town before signing for Sheffield Wednesday but I signed for North End from Brighton. Who am I?

4. What number shirt did Tommy Docherty wear when making his North End debut? a) 4 b) 8 11) 11

5. Scot Symon signed a Preston player when manager of Glasgow Rangers, a player he had signed before, as North End manager. Name the player.

6. What was the attendance when North End won the Old Third

Division Championship by beating Rotherham Utd 3-0 in May 1971? a) 28,244 b) 31,040 c) 27,420

7. Name the North End full-back who once played centre-forward for North End in an FA Cup tie at Sunderland?

8. Which player did not score 3 goals against Cardiff City in the 9-0 win back in 1966? a) Dawson b) Godfrey c) Hannigan

9. Who was the manager the last time North End won the FA Cup?

10. Who was the player who cost North End a reputed fee of £80,000 in the late 1980's but never played for the first eleven?

11. I was born in Blackburn and have played for Sheffield United, Halifax, Burnley, Rotherham, Mansfield and Doncaster as well as North End. I am now at Macclesfield. Who am I?

12. Was his room ill? (Anagram of popular well-travelled NorthEnd player).

Notes

158

Notes

160